Guide to Non-Ferrous Metals and their Markets

Peter Robbins and John Edwards

Kogan Page, London/Nichols Publishing Company, New York

First published in Great Britain in 1979 by
Kogan Page Limited, 120 Pentonville Road, London N1 9JN
Second revised edition published in 1980

Reprinted 1981

British Library Cataloguing in Publication Data
Robbins, Peter
    Guide to non-ferrous metals and their markets. — 2nd ed.
    1. Nonferrous metal industries
    I. Title II. Edwards, John, b. 1935
    338.4'7'669   HD9539.A2
    ISBN 0-85038-302-1

Published in the United States of America in 1979, 1980
by Nichols Publishing Company, Post Office Box 96,
New York NY 10024

Library of Congress Cataloging in Publication Data
Robbins, Peter
    Guide to non-ferrous metals & their markets
    1. Nonferrous metal industries. 2. Market surveys.
    I. Edwards, John, joint author. II. Title.
    HD9539. A2R6 1980 380. 1'45'669 78-20656
    ISBN 0-89397-096-4

Printed in Great Britain by
Anchor Press, Tiptree, Essex

Contents

Appendices

List of diagrams and price graphs

Acknowledgements

The authors would like to record their thanks for
the help provided in preparing this book notably to
Ethel de Keyser, also to David Young, Sandy Young,
Nancy White and Carol Steiger. We also wish to
thank the Metal Bulletin for providing statistics.

Part 1:
Production, Development and Marketing

Introduction: The Role of Non-Ferrous Metals

Of the 100 or so known elements over 80 are metallic. Each metal has its own definite physical characteristics but not all metals have found an important role in industry. This may be because no use has yet been found for them, or that another cheaper metal with similar properties is employed, or that the metal is so poisonous that it cannot be mined, processed, or handled without creating environmental hazards.

Conversely, there are some metals, even quite rare ones, that have achieved a massive importance in technology and are indispensable in modern civilization.

This book is concerned with metals that are commercially important enough to sustain a regularly traded market but it excludes the precious metals, that is gold, silver and the platinum group metals. The markets of these metals are governed as much by currency fluctuations and investment considerations, as by supply from mines and consumption by industrial consumers.*

Each metal dealt with in this book has its own market idiosyncrasies. For anyone who wishes to follow these markets, this book can only be a primer and a guide. In order to understand why a market behaves as it does on a given day the various metal trade periodicals need to be studied and there should be regular exchanges with merchants who daily trade the particular metal.

Price influences

Prices are affected by demand, supply, exchange rate fluctuations, strikes, wars, technical innovations, environmental considerations, the price of fuel, changes in stockpile limits, new mines, freight rates, and perhaps more important than all these in the short-term, the judgement or even the whim of the merchant, producer, consumer or investor.

The smaller the market for a metal, the more susceptible it is to manipulation. Selenium, for instance, has a world production of only about 1,000 metric tons. At $12.00 per lb it would theoretically cost less than $30 million to buy the entire world output of this metal with

* See *Guide to Precious Metals and their Markets,* Kogan Page Ltd

no chance of production being increased because selenium is a by-product of copper production. Selenium is essential in the production of photocopying machines amongst other things. Could it be that for the comparatively small investment of $30 million, an investor could threaten to bring to a halt the world's photocopying machine industry, or at least force that industry to pay almost any price for its selenium supplies?

In practice, this could not quite happen because of the difficulty of buying enough metal without others knowing about it. But by buying 20 or so tons of selenium at a time, the market would go up by at least $1.00 per lb. This type of risky speculation has taken place many times particularly in periods of natural shortage.

Most of the metals dealt with in this book, however, are not by-products. They are mined in their own right. But for many of these metals this has not freed the markets from short-term manipulation by merchants and producers alike.

Surprisingly, perhaps, there is little investment interest in metals that are not traded formally on one or other of the world's commodity exchanges. This may be due partly to the volatility of the markets or to the specialized knowledge required to deal successfully.

In the copper market for example, non-metal trade investors including banks, insurance companies and pension funds, are prepared to support the market when its value goes too far below cost price. This is because copper is traded on a futures market which has had a good record of utilizing available investment funds.

There is, however, next to no chance of including many rare metals in such formal commodity exchanges in the foreseeable future. The worldwide turnover is far too small to justify the cost of such an operation.

The markets of some of the rarer metals are greatly distorted in relation to the true supply/demand factors. These metals are by-products of the production of other less rare metals, which means that however great the demand for the by-product, production cannot be increased to meet this demand without a similar rise in demand for the major product.

There is an apparent limit to this state of affairs when the value of the by-product exceeds the value of the major product in a given volume of ore, but this is an extremely rare occurrence as most by-product metals only constitute a small percentage of the major production.

The application of these metals is often extremely sophisticated. They may be part of an alloy forming a minute but integral part of a jet engine, or chemical process, or an electronic device in which the value of the metal used represents an insignificant part of the cost of the entire system in which it is used. This means that if no substitute is available, the price of the metal can rise by several hundred per cent before it has any effect on the competitiveness of the consumers' product.

These factors help to create erratic, volatile markets.

In times of high demand, producers are unable to increase output and consumers are not concerned with the price they pay. In the recent past, the price of cobalt, cadmium, molybdenum and indium (to give typical examples of by-product metals) have displayed price rises of around 500 per cent in times of high demand which have lasted a few months at a time. These metals have markets that are more volatile than any other commodity or investment market in the world.

To add to the difficulties of predicting future consumption and the uses of such metals, there are other factors to consider. For instance, technicians are inventing new uses for rare metals every day, particularly in the electronics and chemical industries. An obscure piece of research could, one day, result in an important new use for a rare metal as a semi-conductor or as a catalyst. Furthermore, reserves of metal in the earth's crust are finite and the costs of extracting, refining and distributing metals rise each year, with a consequent increase in the risk of investment in metal production.

Alloys

Very few metals are used in their pure state. They are used instead as alloys: a combination of two or more metals. There is an almost limitless permutation of alloys but the most important are those consumed in massive quantities by the steel industry. These are known as bulk ferro-alloys and are the alloys of iron with chrome, silicon and manganese. The markets for each of these alloys are so large that they exceed the markets for most pure metals and represent the most commonly traded form of the three metals concerned. Other ferro-alloys such as ferro-nickel, ferro-titanium and ferro-molybdenum, are also important enough to have their own independent market.

The only other types of alloy to have an international market are those based on zinc, copper, nickel and aluminium.

The future

As with fossil fuels, the demand for non-ferrous metals is growing while their reserves are finite and the cost of production is rising. This obviously means that in the long term prices must rise.

The prices of most metals have increased considerably in the last year or so from the rather low levels which obtained between 1975 and 1978. These rises were caused by a number of factors. The growth in production capacity had been curtailed due to the previous low level of prices, while demand remained reasonably high. There was an unprecedented increase in speculative buying from outside the metal industry and this occurred at a time when investment from real estate and the world's stockmarkets was yielding low rates of return and the value of the dollar was rapidly declining. The interest in base metal buying was also stimulated by a spectacular rise in precious metal prices.

However, the major economic recession developing in 1980 brought a decline in the consumption of metals. Speculators were discouraged from buying metals while interest rates remained high. But if concern about the value of the major currencies grows or there is a further deterioration in the world's political climate, speculative buying interest may support metal prices during the recessionary period.

The past few years have also witnessed a growing tendency for producers to take greater control of metal prices. This can be done more effectively when a single producer is responsible for a very large share of the world's production of a particular metal. China, for instance, is now exercising a great deal of control over the world's antimony and tungsten price. Zaire and Zambia have successfully increased the price of cobalt by some 400 per cent (the shortage was of course first created by the rebel invasion into Zaire in 1978), and the mercury price has been controlled to some extent by the major producers of that metal. This trend will continue but in periods of low demand it is more difficult to restrict the sales of metal in order to increase the price.

There is evidence that the major powers are taking a greater interest in future supplies of strategically important metals. France, Germany and the United Kingdom are all at various stages of setting up a stock-pile of metals and minerals. The USSR has been a major long-term purchaser of metals and there are signs that United States foreign policy is taking metals supplies into greater account especially in relation to the third world.

This book seeks to explain in a non-technical way how non-ferrous metals are obtained, what they are used for, and how they are sold. It also covers the many influences that affect the supplies and prices of metals. An alphabetical review of the individual metals (pages 65-180) provides a detailed description of the supply and demand position, an historical background of marketing and pricing, as well as a look at probable future trends.

Mining, processing, manufacture

If the supply of metals was suddenly to cease, it would not be possible to sustain life as we know it. This dependence is likely to grow rather than lessen as man discovers more and more specialized ways of using metals and minerals in his quest to advance his standard of living. The manufacture of rival materials, such as plastics, is dependent on metals and the use of plastics to replace metals in certain sectors only enlarges the total market and releases metals for other sectors. Without substitution of this kind there would not be enough materials available at the right price.

It can be argued that it is the extent to which mankind can exploit the mineral and metal resources in the earth's crust that regulates progress in our societies. This simply means that these resources are available at a time when man has the skills and capacity to exploit them. If the consumption of metals on a *per capita* basis was the same in the developing world, notably China, as it is in the richer industrialized western world, the quantities required would increase far beyond the present levels.

The mining, processing and manufacture of metals is second only to agriculture worldwide as a provider of employment and earnings. There is a lengthy process between the extraction of metals from the earth to their eventual use in an industrial or consumer product which involves a host of ancillary industries. And before mining the metal, exploration is required to find suitable deposits and their viability needs to be evaluated.

Mining requires a range of machinery and equipment and the provision of an infrastructure, including the possible building of roads, railways and complete townships. Once mined, the next stage is the processing of the ore into concentrates, the smelting and refining of the metals into the form required followed by the shipping to the point of consumption.

Subsequent stages are the marketing and trading of metals involving financial institutions of all kinds; the fabrication of the metals into semi-manufactured form, into alloys or into the many other forms required before it is included in the final product that in turn is distributed and marketed. All these stages involve the provision of employment and earnings.

Mining is no longer under the control of a relatively few powerful groups, based in the richest countries. In the communist bloc, which still has vast untapped resources, it is almost entirely under state control. In most other countries, the host government either directly controls mining activities or has a strong interest, and is the final authority over the policy and behaviour of the mining companies. This increased state control, which often extends far beyond mining and is carried right up to the sale of the metal to the manufacturing industry, means that new criteria are replacing the old economic law of supply and demand. The national and political interests of the country concerned are often given priority over commercial considerations. Developing countries, for example, wish to retain more and more of the processing of their raw material resources in the country of origin to provide more employment and earnings; so the first stage is the shift of smelting and refining facilities away from the industrialized countries — already beset by environmental problems — to the developing areas anxious to create industry. The next logical sequence would be for the semi-manufacturing units to follow, and so on. If this trend continues it will cause a considerable disruption in the present pattern of trade.

Changes in the world metal trade

Developing countries, too, in their quest for a new world economic order are seeking to control sales and marketing of metals to a much greater extent than in the past. With increasing wealth, and with populations growing at a faster rate than in the present industrialized countries, it is likely that the main growth in demand for metals will be concentrated in the developing countries. Some governments will be expected to give special priority to their domestic markets, which will mean a lesser amount available for export.

Linked by a common desire to earn more for their raw material resources, that were sold too cheaply in the past, it is likely that fresh attempts will be made to launch producer cartels in order to control metal supplies and prices in a similar manner to that employed by the oil producing countries. Although such cartels are unlikely to succeed in the long term, they could be a powerful influence in times of shortage, when a lack of investment as a result of low prices or fears about future supplies starts to make itself felt.

The inflation in costs, aggravated by the need to exploit deposits in more remote areas and with less rich ore bodies, in consequence of the exhaustion of existing mines, presents formidable problems. It is now unlikely that any single mining group, however prosperous, will be able to finance the exploitation of a major project single-handed, especially in view of the political risks involved and the increasing demands of host governments.

International consortia, and perhaps the creation of an international fund, will be the new order of the day. The time when new mines could be funded by money loaned against forward sales at a known price are also numbered. Inflation, and fluctuations in the currency rates, make fixed price contracts for forward sales almost impossible, without the inclusion of a host of sub-clauses to deal with all possibilities.

In any event the sanctity of long-term contracts has been brought into disrepute. Governments have refused to honour them either because of a change of government, a change of attitude or simply because changed circumstances mean that the contract conflicts with the national interest of the country concerned.

The need for some form of guaranteed return and the drive for commodity price stabilization generally, as a means of sharing the world's wealth more fairly, are bringing profound changes in the market place. These considerations are overriding the basic law of supply and demand which so far has been the overwhelming influence in the metal markets.

At the same time the growth in international trade has promoted the growth of multinational groups engaged in the buying and selling of metals. Mining companies, faced with governments taking over many of their previous activities, are tending to protect themselves by forming larger and more powerful units. They are also expanding vertically into merchanting, broking and metal manufacturing.

Merchants and broking groups, helped by the vast improvement in communications, have also expanded internationally. They are operating in many countries and markets instead of confining themselves to their domestic situations. The expansion of East-West trade has been due largely to merchants seeking new trading opportunities in the communist bloc countries and attention is now being focused on the developing countries, as importers as well as exporters. The aggressiveness of the major Japanese merchanting groups — often acting in concert and backed by government support — has been a prime influence in expanding merchant activity and importance.

Political significance of distribution, production and consumption patterns

Political considerations are now becoming more important in the metals industry in line with the changing forces in the world. At the start of the industrial revolution trading in metals was largely controlled by the consuming countries, who developed and marketed raw material supplies throughout the world.

This method of control is not new. Similar controls on trading in raw materials were exercised by the Phoenicians, the Romans and later the Spanish and Portuguese. They all brought back riches of one kind or another from countries able to supply their needs.

At one stage Britain, through the Commonwealth and as the largest importer of metals, controlled much of the trade through various big mining companies formed for that purpose. Later rich and powerful mining companies, based in the United States, spread their tentacles throughout the world by investing in the exploitation of metals required to fuel the industrialization of the western world. Powerful mining groups based in other countries also operated internationally, although usually, like the US companies, with a large domestic base for their operations.

Once again the order is changing. The communist bloc countries give priority to their own needs and ambitions, introducing new concepts into world trade. Other raw material supplying countries have become politically independent and seek to control their own destinies and assets; putting their needs before the requirements of the industrialized world.

Independent developing countries are eager to improve their own standard of living by increased industrialization. They are dependent on exports of metals, and other raw materials, for the bulk of their foreign exchange earnings. But more and more metal supplies are likely to come from developing countries as the deposits in the industrialized world become exhausted.

Growing Importance of Developing Countries and the Trend towards International Market Control

There is a growing awareness amongst the countries supplying raw materials that they have been handing over their national resources — unrenewable in the case of metals — to the industrialized countries on terms that have enabled the rich countries to become richer, using resources provided by the poorer countries.

This realization that the industrialized world was waxing fat on raw materials supplied by developing countries, who were becoming poorer as a result, has built up a mood of discontent. It received a further, possibly decisive, push when the oil producing countries' cartel — OPEC, the Organization of Petroleum Exporting Countries — in 1973, exposed the vulnerability of the industrialized world to curbs on a vital raw material and demonstrated that the richer countries could be forced to pay more. Suppliers of other raw materials, including metals, in developing countries were encouraged to emulate the example set by the oil producers and to seek a far greater share of wealth for their resources.

However, it has not proved simple. Oil is in a specially favourable position for a cartel. Its reserves appear to be far more limited than those of many other raw materials. In the long term it is just another form of energy but in the short term the industrialized world is dependent on oil. There is a common political link between the main oil exporting countries that enables them to cooperate far more easily than is usual for suppliers selling the same product. The geographical and political closeness amongst the oil producers has enabled them to form an effective cartel, at least for the time being, and to resist the economic pressure imposed by the industrialized world.

It is far more difficult for developing countries, dependent on metal exports, to control the markets in this manner. The production of most metals is spread over a wider geographical area; much of the present output of metals is in the industrialized countries where the growth of secondary or scrap metals competes with primary supplies; and large percentages of refining and smelting facilities are also concentrated in industrialized countries, since they are highly capital intensive units requiring large investments.

Of primary importance is the fact that with most metals, and indeed most raw materials other than oil, the main exporting countries find it almost impossible to cooperate effectively. Many of these countries have governments which differ in their political outlook and which tend to regard other exporters as rivals in the market place.

Bearing in mind their newly won independence, and the strong sense of nationalism that helped achieve that independence, it is not difficult to see the problems involved in poorer countries cooperating for the common purpose of controlling a market, in the teeth of powerful opposition from the industrialized world on which they are still economically dependent. Many of the developing countries involved simply cannot afford to cut back production of their main source of export earnings without creating unacceptable unemployment levels and poverty in their domestic situations. So they remain subject to the economic ups and downs in the industrialized world where fluctuations in demand — as a result of the rise and fall in industrial activity — to a large extent decide the prices paid to the supplying countries for their metals. Thus during an economic recession it is the developing country supplying raw materials that bears the brunt, since it is often unable to adjust output to the lower level required because of the effect on unemployment and on its foreign exchange earnings.

This vicious circle is completed when surplus production brings prices down to below the cost of output causing heavy losses to the countries least able to afford them. Ironically the success of the oil producers' cartel unleashed the economic recession that demonstrated the fallibility of other raw material suppliers.

Producer cartels

Moves to break out of this stranglehold have been unsuccessful so far. The copper exporters have demonstrated the problems involved in forming a cartel. In 1967 the Intergovernmental Council for Copper Exporting Countries (known by its initials in French, since it is based in Paris, as CIPEC) was formed. It had four founder members — Chile, Peru, Zaire and Zambia — which between them controlled nearly 70 per cent of the world's trade in copper exports, not production, since the biggest producers of copper are the United States and the Soviet Union, who consume their own output domestically.

By 1978 the founder members had been joined by Indonesia as a full member, Australia, Papua New Guinea, Yugoslavia and Mauretania as associate members and Canada as an observer. But CIPEC has totally failed either to control the copper market or to prevent a slump in prices to well below the cost of production levels, despite accounting for the bulk of the world's copper trade.

Political differences between the member countries have not helped. The government in Chile changed radically during the period, with the replacement of the Allende Marxist government by a military dictatorship to which other CIPEC governments were hostile. There have also been disputes between the other member countries, more interested in pursuing their own interests and faced with differing domestic problems. Two major achievements were the agreement to cut back production by 15 per cent at one stage, and persuading the Japanese Government to stop exporting its surplus copper to the world market and thereby depressing prices.

However, the cutback agreement proved to be more transitory than real, since it was based on expected production in order to allow for expansion plans. Some countries were actually exporting larger quantities after the cutback than before, and the impact on market prices soon faded away and respect for CIPEC also suffered a severe blow. The Japanese maintained their export ban. But this entailed the build-up of a huge stockpile, which simply added to the surplus stocks held around the world that had such a depressing influence on prices.

Having failed to make any progress as a producer cartel, copper exporting countries subsequently looked at an alternative method of stabilizing the market in cooperation with consumers.

The model for this alternative type of producer/consumer cooperation is provided by the International Tin Agreement, which has effectively controlled the tin market for over 20 years. In many ways tin is one of the best candidates for a producer cartel, since output is concentrated in six or seven main producing countries, most of which are developing nations with a common interest in raising the price of tin. In addition, three of the most important producing countries — Malaysia, Indonesia and Thailand — are close to each other geographically and face similar political problems. Bolivia, the world's second largest producer of tin, has a constant interest in obtaining price increases since it is a high cost producer compared with Malaysia, having to dig the tin out of mines high up in the unfriendly Andes where oxygen is in short supply and mining conditions, in consequence, very onerous.

There is a long history of control schemes in relation to tin which were originally organized by UK-based mining companies. The price of tin tends to be very volatile and its supply/demand situation is closely linked to trends in the industrialized world through its main outlet, tinplate, which, as part of the steel industry, is highly sensitive to economic changes.

These various schemes met with limited success. They proved costly to operate and did not prevent prices fluctuating wildly. The Tin Producers Association gave way to the International Tin Committee, which attempted to include consumer representatives but they played little part. However, after the Second World War it was decided to make a new effort to control the tin market, combining the forces of the leading producing and consuming countries with equal representation under a new International Tin Agreement. This finally came into force in 1956. Although consumers had equal voting rights, the basic objective of the Tin Agreement is to protect the interests of the tin producing countries. These were clearly set out in the first Agreement, but were enlarged and expanded upon in subsequent Agreements, to take account of the many and various interests involved.

The basic objectives remain as outlined in the preamble to the first Agreement:

'a) to prevent or alleviate widespread unemployment or under-employment and other serious difficulties which are likely to result from maladjustments between the supply of and demand for tin;

b) to prevent excessive fluctuations in the price of tin and to achieve a reasonable degree of stability of price on a basis which will secure long-term stability between supply and demand;

c) to ensure adequate supplies of tin at reasonable prices at all times.'

Objective (c), subsequently modified and enlarged, was essentially a sop to the consumers since no one has yet devised an effective way of preventing prices from rising once a shortage develops. The basic formula of the Agreement is that a buffer stock is created with the purpose of buying up tin when a surplus situation develops and prices threaten to fall below an agreed 'floor' level, at which it becomes uneconomic for producers to continue production. The buffer stock also sells any surplus tin to try and prevent prices going through an agreed 'ceiling' level, above which consumers believe prices are unreasonably high and which will hit demand. Prices for tin were originally the cash quotations on the London Metal Exchange. But in 1972, following the 'float' of sterling, it was decided to use the Straits tin price quoted in Malaysian ringitts as the basis for buffer stock price ranges under the International Tin Agreement. Ideally, under the Agreement, prices should remain in the mid-range at which point the buffer stock does not normally operate. The buffer stock is a net buyer of tin in the lower range. It is the buffer stock manager's task to ensure that the price does not go below the floor and to decide when and how to start buying should the market enter the lower price range. Funds are provided by the member countries.

Once the floor is reached, the buffer stock is supposed to take in all tin offered to it until its financial resources are exhausted. An added protection against the floor price being breached, as has happened in the past, is the International Tin Council which has the power to impose export quotas on the producing countries when the buffer stock holdings reach a certain level.

The imposition of export quotas is a vital key to protecting the all-important guaranteed floor price for tin which is quoted by producers when seeking funds to expand or to maintain production. Quotas provide the fundamental answer to a surplus situation, but they take some time to have an effect and it is therefore important for the buffer stock to retain control in the interim period. For this reason it was agreed in the Fifth International Tin Agreement, which came into force in 1977, that the buffer stock should be doubled in size from the equivalent of 20,000 to 40,000 metric tons. The new total is made up of 20,000 metric tons, compulsorily contributed by the producing countries, who derive the main benefit from the protection of the floor price, plus 20,000 metric tons of voluntary contributions from the consuming countries. It was argued that a larger buffer stock would enable more holdings to be acquired in times of surplus, leaving a larger quantity to be disposed of in times of shortage, when the ceiling price is threatened.

So far commodity agreements of all kinds, including tin, have failed to find a formula whereby prices can be prevented from going through the ceiling. Money is usually available to protect the floor price, possibly with the help of export or production quotas. But shortages force prices up which usually means that there are inadequate supplies available in the buffer stock to prevent the ceiling being breached. Once the buffer stock holdings are exhausted the market is out of the control of the Agreement. There is a built-in disadvantage to consumers anxious to defend the ceiling in that contributions to the Tin Council buffer stock are normally in the form of money, representing the equivalent tonnage of tin, rather than in the form of tin itself. However, in the Fifth Agreement the United States planned to make its voluntary contribution with surplus tin from its strategic stockpile.

Producing countries, however, prefer to make cash contributions since they can then maintain their trade with consumers in the tin itself at what they hope will be a higher price than the nominal value of their buffer stock contributions. This means that the buffer stock normally starts with no surplus holdings of actual tin, unless these are carried over from a previous Agreement.

The shock administered by OPEC in 1973, and the realization of its growing dependence on suppliers of raw materials, persuaded the United States to join the Fifth International Tin Agreement. The Soviet Union had joined the Fourth Agreement and the only major tin producing or consuming country which is not a member at present is China.

Strategic stockpiles

Prior to the United States joining the Agreement it had maintained a large measure of control over the tin market by building up its strategic stockpile of tin to over 350,000 metric tons. This was equivalent to about two years' world consumption at the time when the stockpiling purchase programme ceased in 1955.

Release of surplus tin from the stockpile in times of shortage has helped fill deficits of new production to consumption on several occasions and kept prices under control. The threat of stockpile releases had an equally restraining effect. But on the whole the United States Government cooperated with the International Tin Council in, for example, agreeing not to sell stockpile tin below the market price and not to sell it at all when the buffer stock was engaged in support-buying operations.

Nevertheless the threat of stockpile sales of tin by the world's largest consumer kept a tight rein on the demands of producing countries for upward revisions in the Tin Agreement price ranges. Theoretically, the price ranges, apart from being renegotiated with each new Agreement, are also adjusted in line with the trend in production costs, in order to ensure that producers receive a sufficiently reasonable return so that future supplies will be adequate.

In practice, the state of the market was the major element in deciding whether or not the producers pressed for a rise in the price range. Any rise in the price range has to be voted for by both producing and consuming members. This means that the United States, by reason of being the largest consumer of tin, has a virtual veto on price range increase proposals, much to the bitterness of producing countries. Since the entry of the United States as a member of the Fifth Agreement, debates for rises in the price ranges have become much more political and contentious.

United States membership of the Tin Agreement marked a change in its general hostility to commodity agreements, which until then it had viewed as a form of producer cartel in direct opposition to its anti-trust laws. It also coincided with the United States taking a fresh look at its stockpile policy. The decision was taken to review the basic objectives of the stockpile. Stockpile releases had already been used to hold back price increases not only in tin but in a variety of other raw materials, including copper and nickel. They were also being used increasingly as a means of raising revenue for the United States Government.

Bearing in mind these depradations of the quantities held in certain commodities, and the concern about the future supply of some raw materials, it was decided to revise the stockpile objectives and to base them on anticipated requirements for a three-year (non-nuclear) war. This review produced a completely new set of objectives, including the building up of certain stockpiles, among which were copper and nickel, which had been run down. The copper stockpile had reached over a million short tons (2,000 lbs each) in 1960 and was sold out in 1973 when a nine month strike over a wage claim in the United States domestic producing and refining industry created an acute shortage of supplies.

Another new objective was to cut drastically the stockpile requirements of several metals, including tin and silver. A most important decision was that the stockpile objective for tin was to be cut from 232,000 to 40,000 short tons. The stockpile holdings of tin have been eroded from 350,000 tons in 1955 to around 230,000 short tons in 1968, when stockpile sales were suspended for five years in order to avoid conflicting with the operations of the Tin Agreement.

Sales were resumed again in 1973 as part of a new policy of using the stockpile resources to boost national revenue, with Congress authorizing the sale of 30,000 short tons. By 1978 the stockpile authorities had disposed of the 30,000 short tons, which meant that the stockpile had been reduced to just over 200,000 tons, of which some 160,000 tons had been declared surplus to requirements under the revised stockpile policy. The stockpile objective was subsequently increased by 10,000 to 42,000 tons of tin leaving some 150,000 tons available for disposal.

Many powerful voices in Congress were dubious about the advisability of running the stockpile holdings of tin so low in view of the loss of United States influence in the main tin producing area in the Far East, following the Vietnam war. Allied to this was the fact that tin is one of the few important metals not found in any large quantities on the North American continent.

Eventually in 1980 Congress agreed to the release of a further 35,000 tons of stockpile tin. Of this 5,000 tons was put aside to provide the US voluntary contribution to the buffer stock of the International Tin Council. However, there were considerable complications surrounding this contribution since the buffer stock had not previously received actual supplies of tin; it had always received a cash equivalent to a specified tonnage. The remaining 30,000 tons of stockpile tin was destined for sale, at the rate of 10,000 tons a year, for a three-year period commencing in July 1980. A new method of selling, by tender to the highest bidder, was agreed, to replace the previous method where prices were fixed by the General Services Administration. It was also agreed with the International Tin Council that tin would not be sold below the Tin Agreement price ranges and the US pledged not to disrupt the market. Nevertheless the recommencement of stockpile releases met with considerable opposition from producing countries, especially Bolivia, and soured negotiations for a new Tin Agreement to replace the Fifth Tin Agreement which expires in June 1981.

At the initial tin negotiating conference in April/May 1980 it became apparent that there were fundamental disagreements over the terms of a new pact. Producing countries wanted a greater voting power and control over the Agreement while the US sought to change it substantially by increasing the size of the proposed buffer stock and eliminating export quotas as a means of regulating the market. This first conference for the proposed Sixth Tin Agreement ended in deadlock with neither exporting nor importing countries prepared to give way. It appeared likely that the Fifth Agreement would be extended for one year to provide more time for the resolution of differences. The Tin Agreement is the model commodity pact and has a political importance extending beyond the tin market; strenuous efforts will therefore be made to prevent its dissolution and replacement by a producers' cartel.

UNCTAD

The Tin Agreement is a vital ingredient in the efforts of the United Nations Conference on Trade and Development (UNCTAD) to try and achieve the new economic order demanded by developing countries. It is hoped that by stabilizing commodity prices at higher levels a flow of wealth would be forced from the consumer, industrialized countries to the poorer, supplying countries.

The idea behind the integrated commodities programme, launched by UNCTAD, was for a common buffer stock fund to be created, financed by the richer countries. This is to serve as a back-up for a variety of raw materials where the market needs to be stabilized by artificial means at a higher level in order to provide greater export earnings for the developing countries. Copper and tin are among the key 10 'core' commodities specified by UNCTAD as in need of an international commodity agreement, on the lines of the tin pact, and backed by the common fund instead of each commodity having its own individual buffer stocks.

At first consumer countries, frightened by the example of OPEC, saw commodity agreements between producing and consuming countries as a useful alternative to producer cartels. But then serious doubts began to creep in about the effectiveness of a common buffer stock and international agreements for certain commodities, including copper. The common fund also became the political flashpoint for demands by producing countries for a new economic order giving them a bigger slice of the world's wealth.

Consumer countries argued that a common fund would be extremely expensive, especially if the copper market was included, and probably ineffective in stabilizing markets. They feared that maintaining artificially high prices for a lengthy period would encourage inflation, permit inefficient producers to remain in business and lead to the creation of even bigger, and more costly, surpluses.

Various alternatives have been suggested. These included the creation of national stockpiles, or reserve stocks, held against any shortages of supplies but only loosely linked to any international agreement. Another suggestion was that the export earnings of developing countries should be guaranteed at certain minimum agreed levels instead of the raw materials supplied.

This principle has been incorporated in the Lomé Convention between the European Economic Community and the so-called ACP (African, Caribbean, Pacific) group of developing countries. The idea is that by guaranteeing an agreed export earnings minimum figure — made up by payments from the Community if the country fails to achieve the minimum figure because of low commodity prices or an unpredictable setback in production — the supplying countries will be encouraged to maintain output without the fear of surplus supplies ruining their earnings.

One suggestion is that the EEC as the biggest importer of metals in the world might incorporate copper under the Stabex system of the Lomé Convention. The EEC is also working on plans for an international insurance scheme for mining companies to protect them against developments in supplying countries, which could result in their being nationalized without proper compensation. The threat of this happening, often as a result of a change of government, has brought mining exploration and expansion to a standstill in many areas deemed to be politically unsafe by mining groups and bankers.

Whatever the result of these political confrontations, it is apparent that developing countries which supply the bulk of the world's primary metal exports will play an increasingly important part in controlling the markets. There has already been a wholesale move towards nationalization in most developing countries, either with or without adequate compensation. And host governments now play a far bigger role in the selling and marketing of the production that provides the lifeblood for their economies. This trend will continue as the world becomes more dependent on metals from the developing countries. But the richer industrialized world is unlikely to give in to blackmail by producer countries or cartels. In line with the changing political patterns in the world, non-ferrous metals, as vital ingredients in the process of industrialization and in the acquisition of wealth, will be in the forefront of these political and economic struggles.

Future Supplies
and Pricing Policies

Much has been made in recent years of gloom and doom predictions forecasting that the world will run out of metals and minerals in the future as known reserves become exhausted. Learned studies have apparently proved conclusively that the growth in consumption of metals is outstripping the discovery of new deposits at such a rate that the world will run out of supplies within the next 100 years (and very much sooner in the case of some metals). One particular example cited was mercury (quicksilver), supplies of which, according to one authoritative prediction, should have been exhausted by now.

Certainly the projected growth in demand for metals in the years ahead is frighteningly large, as the world production expands and the demand for better standards of living accelerates.

But the gloom and doom predictions reflect a narrow, naive view. For a start the development of new materials like plastics has already had a profound effect on the consumption of metals and it is reasonable to assume that further developments of this nature will take place in the future. Indeed, optical fibres and micro-electronic 'chips' are existing examples of how industrial societies may be revolutionized and similar developments affecting metals are likely in the near future.

Reclamation

It is often forgotten that many metals, and the products in which they are an element, do not disappear once they have been used. In some cases a large percentage of primary metals taken from the ground are used repeatedly as they are virtually indestructible. When metals are turned into chemicals or powders they normally cannot be reclaimed but, in most instances, metals are recoverable. The supply is simply shifted from below ground to above ground and the 'deposits' above ground are increasing in size all the time.

So far, above the ground 'deposits' have barely been touched. In the case of lead, copper and aluminium, large percentages of total supplies come from secondary or scrap sources in industrialized countries. In these countries, the above-ground deposits have built up over the years and reclaiming techniques have been worked out on an economical basis. In the case of lead, for example, the system created to recover batteries has been highly developed and the bulk of supplies comes from secondary rather than primary sources.

In aluminium and copper a large percentage of total supplies come from scrap sources, and there has been considerable growth in the recovery of alloys that can be used again. But recovery of previously used material depends on its being available in sufficient quantities to be competitive with the primary product. This means that in many parts of the world where consumption is low there is very little recovery of secondary metals because it is not economically justified.

Nevertheless the supplies are there, and will become recoverable in increasing quantities if the right economic stimulus is provided — in other words if the price is right. At the same time increased price incentives would greatly improve the methods of recovering scrap materials, and expand the types of metal reclaimed.

Until now it has not been worthwhile to develop more sophisticated techniques for reclaiming metals. At the moment the reclamation industry relies mainly on crude and simple recovery techniques such as sorting, cutting and the use of a magnet to pick out the steel, as opposed to the non-ferrous parts. Chemical and other modern techniques are not widely employed because they are not often economically viable. But if a shortage of primary supplies did develop, and prices moved to much higher levels, then the economic incentive to recover more scrap metals would obviously become worthwhile and would be exploited. There is a huge hidden supply of reserves in industrialized countries, a fact which is only registered in times of emergency. However, a greater awareness of recovery potential has been building up in recent years. This is linked with the demands of environmentalists for the removal of unsightly waste and for cleaner manufacturing methods.

Pricing

Price is also the key to primary supplies. It should be remembered that in the case of metals, mankind has until now only exploited the one third of the earth's surface that is not covered by the sea. Even that one third has not been fully used; many of the remoter areas like the North and South Pole regions, the Amazon basin and large tracts of Asia and Africa, have not been fully exploited for their mineral and metal reserves. These areas are, in many cases, remote and difficult especially when there are so many easier deposits available. Over the centuries that mankind has been mining minerals, there has been a natural concentration on deposits that are the easiest to exploit since these are the most profitable.

The metal content of the ore is important but by no means the only factor to consider. First the separation of the metals contained in the ore has to be considered. It might be an ore which has too many metals, involving costly separation processes. Ore containing a high proportion of one metal is usually the easiest to handle, since it is then a matter of separating out one metal and throwing the rest away, or finding out whether there are some valuable by-products contained in the ore that justify further separation processes.

The miner also has to consider a host of other influences before deciding whether a deposit is worth exploiting: whether there is sufficient water available, how far down the ore is located, the existing infrastructure, available labour, and transport facilities for carrying the ore or the refined metal product to the place where it can be treated or sold. An increasingly important factor is the political structure of the host government. The political stability of the government can be crucial in deciding whether or not sufficient funds can be raised to finance the project. In other words economic and political considerations are the prime influences in deciding which metal deposits are to be exploited, not necessarily the richness and size of the ore body. Mining efforts, therefore, have been mainly confined to certain known areas, relying primarily on the improvement in extraction techniques to increase output. Indeed many mines have been worked over several times. The waste product, cast aside by the early miners in favour of richer deposits, becomes financially viable for the more modern miner using a more advanced technique. Thus a lower percentage of metal in any ore body makes it worth exploiting by using these more sophisticated extraction techniques.

When these easy deposits become exhausted, the consequent shortage of supplies can be expected to increase the financial incentive sufficiently to make the more difficult and as yet untapped deposits economically viable, as well as encouraging the miner to go further afield. Additional financial incentives may be required to unlock a large part of the sea bed reserves in view of the different mining techniques that would be required. Nevertheless the supplies are there if needed; some might be available at a far cheaper price once the techniques and political complications surrounding sea bed mining have been clarified. The world debate on dividing up offshore rights is not only concerned with fishing: it is equally concerned with setting the pattern for the future mining of the sea bed. Nodules found on the sea bed, for example, are known to contain large quantities of manganese, copper and nickel as well as many other metals and they are fairly easy to collect.

Looking even further ahead mankind has so far barely scratched the surface of the earth's crust in mining for metals and minerals. Going down deeper into the crust would be far more costly. But if a shortage of supplies was threatened there is no doubt that the ways and means would be found of extracting more of the earth's riches by mining to a deeper level than at present.

Fears of shortages are, therefore, based on possible short-term interruptions of supplies rather than on any fundamental long-term threat. The price at which metals are sold is a complex matter. The basic fundamental, often forgotten, is that the 'real' price of any commodity is what the buyer is prepared to pay for it, not how much it costs to mine or to produce. However, the price that the buyer is pre-pared to pay can be affected by a host of influences, some logical, others less logical. At the same time it is true to say that the metal cannot go on being sold at below the cost of production for too long without affecting the flow of production and the expansion of output.

There are two basic methods of pricing used for selling metals. One is the so-called producer price system. Under this system the producer fixes the price at which he is prepared to sell, although in fixing the price he has to take into account the state of the market and the atti-tude of potential buyers, as well as the price of competitive materials and the need to preserve certain outlets.

The producer price system

The producer price system is widely used throughout the world but is most favoured by North American producers and consumers. This is partly because the United States metals industry is more vertically integrated than others. The company mining the metal is very often the same company smelting and refining it. But in the United States the integration is taken several steps further with the mining company owning the semi-fabricator, normally the main buyer, and sometimes also the fabricator's customer, the manufacturer of the final product that is sold to industry or to the general public.

With this kind of captive outlet it is easy to impose a producer price, especially if most of the main competitors in the business have a simi-lar set-up and are therefore likely to have similar cost pressures. Even consumers, who are not owned by mining companies, often favour the producer price system. They believe that it gives them security of supply if the producer is able to charge a reasonable price and, as long as the same price is charged to their competitors, they need have no fear of being undercut.

At the same time a producer price system normally allows for longer-term price forecasting, since the producer seeks to stabilize the price in his own interests. The producer also smooths out the market place fluctuations by gradual increases to take account of the inflation in his production costs, rather than following the day-to-day changes in the supply/demand position. In other words, the producer is prepared not to capitalize on a sudden shortage situation in the hope that he will not have to sell at a loss if and when there is a surplus supply situation. It is a bargain struck between the product and consumer, with the producer offering continuity of supply at a foreseeable price linked to the costs of production, and the consumer offering a regular purchase of the metal at a price agreeable to the producer.

The producer price system is used in one form or another for almost every metal. There are some notable exceptions, such as tin, which is controlled by the International Tin Agreement, tungsten ore, and other so-called 'minor' metals where production is scattered amongst many small producers with no leading company powerful enough to set a producer price.

'Free market' system

But the producer price system is often used hand in hand with the other main method of pricing metals — the free market system. Free market prices are essentially defined as those not fixed by producers, though as suppliers of the metals producers must have a considerable influence on the free market value. Free markets tend to be controlled by merchants who are able to draw on supplies from non-producer price sources. These include communist bloc or other producers not participating in the producer price system; consumers reselling supplies they do not require; secondary or re-refined metals; and purchases made by the merchants from producers in the producer price system possibly at a discount.

Many metals have two prices: the producer price and the free market price. The free market price is often the price of residual supplies of the metal over and above the regular contracted supplies from the main producer, using a producer price system. In times of shortage, the free market price is above the producer price as buyers seek additional supplies which they are unable to obtain from the producers they normally use. In times of surplus supplies the free market price is at a discount to the producer price in order to attract buying interest.

The importance of the free market in each metal varies considerably. For a start it depends on the share of the total market controlled by the leading suppliers using a producer price system. If, for example, there is a dominant supplier in the communist bloc, who is unwilling to participate in any producer price system adopted by the leading western world producers, then the free market can be most important as a pricing medium for the metal. This is the case with tungsten ore, for which China is the main producer and there is no dominant western world producer able to fix a producer price.

Market situations affecting the normal supply/demand position can also increase the importance of the free market compared with producer price sales. This was the case with nickel when lengthy strikes at the main producer mines in Canada meant that consumers had to turn to the free market for supplies.

With all metals if there is a shortfall in the normal supplies available from producers under the producer price system, the free market often assumes a more important role. For this reason many consumers, whose factories would be forced to close if they could not obtain supplies of the metals required, like to keep their options open by purchasing a percentage of their supplies from free market sources in addition to their regular supply contracts with producers at the producer price. By so doing they gain some benefit when free market prices are low. They can also expect to be given some sort of priority from their free market suppliers when a shortage situation develops. If this line of communication was not kept open the free market suppliers would be tempted to discard their 'panic' orders when supplies were short or charge a premium price over that charged to their regular customers.

Nickel provides another example of the changing relationship between the free market and producer price systems. The surge in production of nickel during the mid-1970s, including the entry of several new producers, created a huge surplus of supplies since demand was badly hit by the economic recession triggered off by the 1973 oil crisis. International Nickel of Canada, which at one time accounted for some 80 per cent of total sales and was, therefore, able to fix an effective producer price, was forced, in 1977, to abandon quoting official prices in favour of 'confidential' prices in an effort to win back some of the sales lost to its competitors. It reinstated official producers at the beginning of 1979 when surplus stocks were cut back as a result of a lengthy strike, but it now faces price competition from the London nickel futures market introduced in April 1979.

Scarcity and surplus

Surplus situations have from time to time created similar distortions in the prices charged for other metals — aluminium and zinc are two such examples.

As regards zinc, the producer price level has had to be adjusted downwards in line with the move in the free market to remain competitive. This was particularly necessary since the producer price is also used as the basis for assessing the cost of ore concentrates bought by the smelters for refining into zinc metal. If heavy discounts are made on the producer price at which the metal is sold, smelters not controlled by mine producers could not afford to buy their raw material intake at a cost based on unrealistically high producer price quotation.

Producers using the producer price system, in fact, can often lose both ways. They are expected, in times of scarcity, to continue supplying consumers at the reasonable contracted prices laid down and not to take too much advantage of scarcity by moving their prices to a much higher level on the free market. However, in times of surplus, producers are under great pressure from consumers to reduce their prices in order to be competitive with free market supplies, which buyers fear may enable their rivals to cut manufacturing costs. Faced with these demands the producer is often forced to give sizeable discounts on his official quotation, although he is supposed to stick to the official price during times of shortage.

The prime argument, however, against the producer price system is that it can be inflexible and not anticipate or recognize the changing situation in the market. The price stability provided is in itself a target for competitors to shoot at and also encourages a lack of enterprise by both producers and consumers.

'Free market' trading

In contrast, the uncertainty of fluctuating free market prices gives a stimulus to both sides to search for the greatest efficiency. This provides the best protection against competition. The free market, in addition, gives a valuable guide to what is happening, and what is likely to happen, in the market place. In some instances the influence of free market forces is so great that they are dominant over the producer price system. This is the case with copper and lead, as well as with several of the 'minor' metals (that is, metals not traded on the London Metal Exchange) such as tungsten and, nowadays, cobalt and quicksilver. Producer prices are fixed in the United States for copper and lead and indeed virtually all metals, but these are influenced by movements on the London Metal Exchange markets and on Comex (the New York copper futures market). In the rest of the world the so-called producer prices are in fact based on the London Metal Exchange quotations. The pricing formulae used in the direct supply contracts between copper and lead producers and their customers are based on the Metal Exchange quotations. This is also the case in supply contracts between merchants and their customers, between suppliers of copper and lead ore concentrates to smelters and refiners, and between scrap dealers and secondary refiners.

Outsiders find this situation difficult to understand, since it is generally considered that producers — and exporting countries — should be able to fix the prices of their own products and must find it difficult to operate and plan ahead if their returns are subject to wild fluctuations governed by the market place. Similarly consumers find it difficult to plan ahead not knowing the price of raw material intake, which in some cases has a sizeable influence on the cost of the final product, especially for fabricators of semi-manufactured products.

These criticisms of the free market system are all valid. Indeed, there is great concern that the activities of non-trade speculators, whose motives have little connection with the metals industry, should on occasion play a major part in influencing price trends.

There is one basic answer. No one has yet been able to devise a better system for fixing copper and lead prices. There have been several attempts to introduce an international producer price system for copper, first of all by American producers, and later by African and Chilean producers. Possibly the most determined attempt was made in the early 1960s when producers, through market support operations, kept the London Metal Exchange copper price at £234 per ton for nearly two years until the end of 1963. This was followed by a multi-price system whereby the Metal Exchange values were allowed to find their own level, but African and Chilean producers pegged their export prices at a lower level as a safeguard against the substitution of copper by other materials. But this system collapsed in 1966 when Chile decided to increase its export price by £160 to nearly £500 per ton and a few weeks later Rhodesia closed the export route for Zambian copper via the railway to ports in Mozambique. Since that unhappy experience, copper producers have given up trying. The cause has subsequently been taken up by CIPEC (the Intergovernmental Council for Copper Exporting Countries) and the United Nations Conference on Trade and Development (UNCTAD).

But their efforts are aimed more at stabilizing prices, especially with a minimum level, by the use of buffer stock operations to buy up surplus supplies in a similar way to the International Tin Agreement.

The chaos in the market place during the 1970s, as a result of the breakdown of the Bretton Woods fixed exchange rate system and runaway inflation in the industrialized countries, undermined the whole concept of fixed prices, and producers have been forced to make frequent changes to remain competitive with the free market. In 1978 there was a major change when Kennecott, the largest United States' copper producer, decided to abandon their producer price system in favour of basing their prices on the New York copper market (Comex) quotations. A similar change was made by another leading US producer, Anaconda, which meant that other producers were forced to introduce more flexible pricing arrangements for their copper.

Supporters of the free market system for metals argue that it is the fairest way of deciding the 'real' price. They point out that production costs vary enormously from country to country and from company to company, so that unless the producer price is based on the highest cost of production, some producers will inevitably face constant losses. For many minor metals produced as by-products during the processing and refining of the major metal, the price obtained by the producer is based, in effect, on how much he can get. Movements in the price of these metals have no direct impact on the supply situation.

The scrap industry

In the case of copper and lead, as well as aluminium, there is another very important influence to be taken into account — that is the growing secondary and scrap industry. Supplies of scrap metal have a totally different cost structure from primary metals, although the end product may be interchangeable. Scrap prices are linked closely to primary metals, since they cover virtually the same product obtained from other sources. However, since it is a substitute for the original metal, scrap tends, on the whole, to be cheaper, although this is not always the case. On occasions scrap supplies may be scarce, while primary supplies are abundant and buyers, whose processes are geared to using secondary metals, might have to pay more. In fact supplies of scrap are also subject to both political and economic influences. Most industrialized countries are reluctant to allow the export of their domestically produced scrap in view of the import savings gained from not having to buy so much primary metal. In consequence, restrictions have been imposed on exports of scrap, which is another reason why it tends to be somewhat cheaper for the domestic consumer who may be the only available buyer. This is also due to the fact that scrap merchants are not equipped with as efficient transport facilities as mine producers who export to a range of countries.

Scrap recovery from the 'mine' above the ground has a totally different cost structure from the mining of primary metals. Scrap refiners rely on the margin between the price at which they buy their raw material intake — either from industrial sources or via collections from the general public — and the price at which they sell the refined product. It is this margin of profit that is all important, not whether the price is high or low. Indeed, in boom times, scrap refiners often do less well since they have to pay far higher prices for their raw material intake and their profit margin is squeezed compared with more depressed times when the margin can be more easily expanded. During times of economic depression the scrap industry is affected by a cutback in supplies, as opposed to a build-up in primary metals. Reduced industrial activity means less investment by companies who normally generate the bulk of scrap supplies when replacing old equipment with new, or when operating at a higher capacity rate and producing more waste residues.

Aluminium producers, operating on a higher international scale than other metal groups, have managed to acquire and retain a large measure of control over both primary and scrap supplies. This is in part due to the fact that, as owners of a large proportion of the fabricating and manufacturing end of the industry, they are also major buyers and, in addition, own a large part of the aluminium secondary refining industry.

But there is not the same integration for copper and lead producers outside the United States and Canada. In the past, lead producers have managed to control the free market prices by support-buying operations, organized amongst themselves. But government disapproval of cartel activities of this kind, especially the anti-trust laws in the United States which are rigorously enforced to prevent collusion amongst producers, has made it more and more difficult for lead producers to operate together, even on international markets.

Copper producers face the same problems of cooperation amongst themselves in a task of much greater magnitude. The quantities and sums involved in the copper industry are very large compared with lead, and the finance required for an effective support-buying policy to control the market would be enormous, and certainly beyond the scope of producers unless backed by government or by international financial resources. Not only is there the cost of actually buying the copper, but also the cost of storage and of having large sums of money tied up for an indefinite period. Many buffer stock operations, including that of the International Tin Agreement, have made money on 'paper'. But a different picture may emerge if the loss from inflation and the lack of interest earned over the period is taken into account.

These hidden costs emphasize the point that influences on the price of metals are not confined to those facing the producer. Political developments worldwide and in specific sensitive areas such as wars, economic trends, interest rates, inflation and changes in currency rates also have to be taken into consideration by buyers and sellers of metals. Reaction to these developments is often more reliably reflected by speculators, who are more sensitive on occasions to the non-trade influences at work. Prices arrived at as a result are the common denominator of all the influences at work, bringing together all the fears and forecasts about future and existing attitudes in deciding the point at which sellers agree to sell and buyers to buy — that is the market price.

Futures Markets:
Hedging and Price Fixing

Futures markets for base metals are confined to London and New York and to only a few base metals — copper, tin, lead, zinc and more recently aluminium and nickel. The collectively defined 'minor' metals have no central marketing place. Price levels are imposed either by producers or by merchants trading in the free markets amongst themselves, and with both producers and consumers. There is speculation in these minor metals, but it is more difficult than in the 'paper' futures market and is mainly confined to those actually dealing in the metal as a producer or consumer but, most commonly, as a merchant.

Without the benefit of hedging facilities the merchant, in particular, has constantly to be alert to changes in the supply/demand position of the various metals. On occasions he has to back his judgement by taking a 'long' or 'short' position that might entail considerable financial risk. He also has to be vigilant to spot occasions when a merchant, a producer or a consumer, attempts to manipulate the market in his favour by buying or selling supplies.

A Minor Metals Traders Association was formed in 1973 by London traders. Several of their European counterparts subsequently joined the Association in an attempt to bring more order to the free markets by establishing some standardization of contracts and of trading regulations. To a large extent trading is dominated by the large groups, often subsidiaries of mining groups and with strong connections on the London Metal Exchange, and with secondary metal dealers.

The mixture of producer prices and merchant-inspired free market trading makes trends in minor metals difficult to follow in what are sometimes highly specialized markets. Fundamentally the trends follow the pattern of industrial and economic activity affecting consumer demand, although movements can often be highly exaggerated.

There are two main futures markets for metals: the London Metal Exchange and Comex. The London Metal Exchange has markets for copper, tin, lead, zinc and silver. It introduced an aluminium contract in October 1978 and a nickel contract in April 1979. The other main metal futures exchange, Comex, is in New York: it has flourishing copper, silver and gold markets, but a zinc futures contract, introduced in 1978, has attracted very little support and is virtually dormant.

The two markets strongly influence each other since, both in theory and in practice, dealers can make a guaranteed profit by selling in one market and buying in the other if prices move out of line on either side of the Atlantic. These arbitrage operations, as they are known, have to take account of the cost of shipping the metal across the Atlantic, currency exchange rate fluctuations and timing, as well as interest rates and storage facilities. But these are quickly calculated by alert traders and any abnormal difference between London and New York copper or silver prices is usually quickly eliminated by the dealers specialising in arbitrage. Arbitrage operations are frequently 'paper' transactions invoking the possibility of shipping the physical metal rather than actually doing so.

On occasions, such as a dock strike or some other domestic development, prices in the two markets can stay out of line for a longer period if metal supplies cannot be made available to the market where prices are highest. Generally the opening of the Comex market in New York, which corresponds with the early afternoon in Europe, has an important influence on the London market, which in turn affects the trend in Comex. It depends on the stronger influence at the time: whether the New York market is dominant in reacting to some development or rumour emanating from the United States, or whether developments affecting London prices are more powerful. Fundamentally the London Metal Exchange is the more influential of the two markets. Although turnover on the New York copper market is usually larger than in London it tends to be speculative to a far greater extent. This is because much of the copper traded in the United States was, traditionally, sold under the producer price system. Comex essentially influenced only what is known as 'merchant' copper which is mainly imported together with other supplies of copper acquired by merchants outside the producer price system.

Many of the fabricators, owned by the big mine producing companies, rely almost exclusively on producer price copper. However, they have to watch price movements on Comex to ensure that their competitors both domestic and foreign are not able to buy copper at a lower price. Traditionally United States domestic buyers of copper have relied on the producers to provide competitively priced copper and, most importantly, a regular flow of such supplies under long-term contracts. Comex was regarded as a speculators' gambling den, since a large proportion of the turnover came from the powerful commodity broking firms and commission houses using funds obtained from private and trade speculators who were seeking to make a profit by correctly anticipating the upward or downward move in prices.

However, a major change came in 1978 when the largest United States copper producer — Kennecott — decided to abandon the producer price system and instead based its selling price for copper cathodes on the Comex spot quotation. It charged an additional sum to cover the cost of delivery since the Comex price is ex-warehouse in New York while Kennecott delivers its copper supplies direct to the customer. The company took this radical step to recapture sales lost to cheaper-priced imports. Other producers were, as a result, forced to adapt their pricing policy.

The importance and respectability of Comex has grown in recent years. The United States has gradually become more dependent on imported supplies of copper as a result of consumption growing at a faster rate than domestic production. At the same time the growth of international trade and communications has meant that the United States industry has become more aware of the opportunities outside North America, and the increasing competition facing its manufacturing companies. The activities of speculators have also become more significant with the changes in exchange rates, even of the previously mighty dollar, following the collapse of the Bretton Woods monetary fixed exchange rate system, the oil crisis and the surge in inflation. Political developments outside the United States are also having a much more profound effect on metal prices and supplies. This is reflected in the price movements on Comex.

These influences have, of course, also heightened the importance of the London Metal Exchange as a price fixing medium. The Metal Exchange, which celebrated its centenary in 1977, is the most powerful influence on the prices of copper, lead and to a lesser extent tin and zinc, outside North America. Its daily price quotations — usually the settlement price at the close of the morning trading session — are used as the basis of the direct supply contracts between producers and consumers of copper and lead. The quotations are not only used to price transactions in refined metal, but also as a basis for pricing ores, concentrates, semi-manufactured products, manufactured metals and scrap.

The bulk of the international trade in copper and lead is handled through contracts negotiated by the producers with the consumers. But these negotiations usually conducted, in the case of copper, during the 'mating season' — that is in the last quarter of the year — basically deal with the quantity to be supplied during the following year. The price at which the copper is to be bought is based on a formula using the Metal Exchange quotations. This may be, as in Japan and Australia, a producer price that is altered according to changes in the Metal Exchange quotations. Or it may be a much more complicated formula whereby the consumer has a specified period during which he can choose to 'price' the copper being delivered to him using the Metal Exchange quotations during that period. One concession given by producers, for example, known as 'back pricing', is the ability of consumers to fix the price of metals supplied on a chosen date for a limited period prior to the delivery date.

Hedging

An advantage of using the Metal Exchange quotations in these contracts is that the consumer can effectively hedge himself against price fluctuations during the period from which he has priced the copper, to the time when it is manufactured and sold at a previously agreed price.

Producers too can hedge against price fluctuations by making matching purchases of copper committed for future sale, thus ensuring that if the price moves down in the meantime they will benefit from the profit made on the futures market, to compensate for the loss made on the physical metal sold. If the price goes up, then the loss on the futures transaction cancels out the extra profit made on the physical sale. Hedging is an insurance, not a speculation.

It is a valuable protection for all sectors of industry, notably the merchants, whose business could be wiped out by an unpredictable price fluctuation even though the company may be run most efficiently. In other words, it enables the company to get on with its business activity without worrying too much about price fluctuations.

In some respects, therefore, it can be argued that it is speculation to reject the use of hedging where it is possible, since there is a risk in judging the price trends correctly, unless it is a 'back to back' deal under which a matching purchase and sale is made on the same terms.

The Metal Exchange is an unusual commodity futures market. Unlike other futures markets it has an important role in the physical trading of metals. Business on the normal commodity futures market and indeed on Comex is usually confined mainly to 'paper' transactions dealing in future delivery dates and cancelling out any commitment to buy or sell by a matching sale or purchase before the delivery date falls due. Non-trade speculators are not geared to take delivery of a metal and are certainly not able to supply any metal they might have agreed to sell. They must therefore cancel any commitment before the delivery date. The trade also uses futures markets as a means of hedging and price fixing, rather than a source of supply, since the metal or commodity deliverable under the contract is often not of the type required by the purchaser. Normally only a small percentage of total turnover is represented by physical trading; the opportunity to make actual purchases and sales is only there as a back-up to the 'paper' trading — a final guarantee or commitment by the user of the market.

The London Metal Exchange

The Metal Exchange is an important source of supply for the metals traded, especially copper. It has warehouses dotted throughout Europe — mainly in Britain, Belgium and Holland. These warehouses, usually situated close to the main ports, hold stocks of the brands of metal authorized by the Metal Exchange to be delivered against the contract specifications.

At one stage, producer supply contracts with consumers used to include a clause forbidding the resale of their copper brands on the Metal Exchange. This was to prevent consumers depressing the market by delivering producer copper into the warehouses and then buying it back at a lower price. But this restriction was swept away by the huge build-up of surplus stocks after the 1974 boom. Surplus copper stocks in the warehouses climbed from around a bare 10,000 metric tons during the period of great scarcity in 1974 to over 640,000 metric tons by 1978. This represented a major source of additional supplies, equivalent to the annual production of Zambia at the time. It was available to consumers over and above the normal supplies provided by producers. The Metal Exchange is a market of last resort for both producers and consumers. It is the ultimate dumping ground for any surplus production and is also the alternative source of supplies for consumers when faced with a shortfall, for whatever reason, from their normal suppliers. One major advantage of buying via the Metal Exchange is that the contract does not include any *force majeure* clause, unlike the producer contracts. So the buyer can be sure of obtaining his purchase, whatever happens, unlike producer supplies where deliveries are often cut back as a result of strikes, production disruptions or other dislocations that come under the *force majeure* clause.

For this reason, and to avoid too much dependence on producers, consumers like to buy some of their supplies on a regular basis via the Metal Exchange. This enables them to top up supplies when required and also to sell off surplus holdings to the merchants forming the bulk of the Metal Exchange membership. Ring-dealing members of the Exchange, in fact, incorporate the interests of many of the leading producers, but they have to observe the same contract regulations as the other non-producer controlled members. The Exchange exists mainly for the merchants, who play an influential role in promoting trade across political barriers and ensuring the distribution of metal supplies where they are needed. Since merchants are often at risk — they are forced to take a position rather than rely entirely on back-to-back deals — the hedging facilities provided by the Exchange are crucial to their operations, giving them a much greater flexibility in serving their customers. Producers often use the Exchange's reservoir of supplies to avoid declaring *force majeure* and thereby tempting the customer to move elsewhere. One difficulty, however, is that many customers buy copper from a particular producer because of the quality of the brand which suits their particular needs. The brand bought via the Metal Exchange cannot be guaranteed, except that it meets the quality specifications laid down under the contract. Brands have to be registered with the Metal Exchange by the producer. They are then checked to make sure that the quality specifications of the contract are met before registration is authorized.

Under the Metal Exchange contracts there is a seller's option. This means that the seller has the choice of brand and warehouse from which he will make available the metal purchased by the buyer. However, premiums and discounts are negotiated for different brands, and it is usually possible for the dealer to switch sales and purchases around to the most convenient warehouse for the buyer. Trading is in warrants, specifying the quantity and type of brand, which the buyer presents to the warehouse when he wishes to take delivery. He then arranges transport for the metal from the warehouse to his factory or to another destination — possibly to be transhipped to another buyer. The warrants are the currency used by the Metal Exchange dealers, and are often used as collateral for bank loans or financial guarantees. The warrants are freely transferable.

Warehouse facilities are strictly regulated by the London Metal Exchange secretariat to ensure that the metal is stored in suitable conditions and that it tallies with the quality and brands specified in the warrants issued by the warehouse managers. Each week the Exchange reports variations in the size of stocks held in the warehouses and this can be an important influence on the market prices.

The Exchange warehouses are the central point at which the residual supplies, not immediately required by consumers, are held and these provide a good barometer of the overall state of the market. In times of surplus the stocks in the warehouses build up and depress the market price. In times of scarcity they dwindle and this forces prices up, often creating a 'backwardation' — that is when the spot or cash price for metal, immediately available from the warehouse, is at a premium to the price of metal for delivery at some time in the future. When the cash price moves to a premium over the three months quotation, it usually means that there is a shortage of supplies worldwide, although on occasions there can be technical squeezes on supplies created by shipping delays to Europe or a sudden surge in demand, which cannot be immediately met. The fundamental principle of the Exchange is that prices go up and down to reflect and eventually correct the supply/demand balance. If there is a shortage, prices go up to the level at which any surplus stocks available will come to the Exchange, and producers will be encouraged to step up output. In times of surplus, the build-up stocks in the warehouses depress prices and discourage production whilst stimulating demand. That is the theory although it does not always work in practice.

The Metal Exchange warehouses are amongst the cheapest and easiest places in the world to store surplus metal supplies. The attraction of putting copper and the other metals traded on the Exchange into the warehouses is that the burden of financing them can be shifted from the producers' or consumers' shoulders. When there are adequate supplies there is normally a 'contango' on the market – that is, the cash price is a discount to the forward quotation; the opposite of backwardation. The gap between the cash price and forward quotation in a contango situation is regulated by the current interest rate in financial markets. This represents the cost of carrying the metal, or holding it in stock, over the period concerned. Banks and other financial institutions help finance the stocks by using what is in effect a guaranteed profit equivalent to or sometimes slightly above the inter-bank interest rate. The procedure is that the bank buys metal at the ruling cash price, and sells at the higher three months price exactly the same quantity of metal for delivery in three months time. It then delivers the metal bought at the lower cash price in three months time against the sale made.

The difference between the lower cash price at which the purchase is made compared with the sale at the higher three months price is the guaranteed profit. Storage and insurance charges for holding the metal at the warehouse (the bank only takes delivery of the warrant) and the brokers' commission have to be deducted. When these deductions from the profit are made they equal the interest rate required to make the proposition sufficiently attractive. This limits the size of any contango, because once it becomes more profitable than the current interest rate, money flows in until it is no longer out of line. Transactions of this kind are known as 'borrowing' from the market.

In a backwardation situation supplies of metal are attracted to the market by the prospect of being able to sell at a higher price and buy back the equivalent amount for delivery at a future date. This is known as 'lending' to the market. The size of the backwardation is theoretically unlimited although it is normally controlled by lending of metal even if there is an overall shortage. Speculators also play a helpful and sometimes vital role in providing financial resources to the market. If a metal is considered to be cheap, speculators are tempted to buy in anticipation of its price going up and generating a useful profit. Speculators tend to prefer buying rather than selling, since it is easier to grasp the concept of buying something one does not want (or of which one does not intend to take delivery) rather than selling something one does not possess. There is a certain logic in this, in that with a sale (or going short as it is known) the sky may be the limit if the price rockets up, especially if one is caught in a technical supply squeeze and has to pay enormous premiums to meet the market commitment by making a matching purchase.

With a purchase (going long) at least the metal bought will always have some value, even if it may be considerably below the price at whch it was bought. The attraction of funds from speculators and financial institutions is that they are, in effect, helping to finance surplus stocks, a burden which would normally be carried by producers. At the same time speculative investment in metals, as a safeguard against inflation, currency changes or simply in order to make a profit, means that more money is flowing into the metals industry.

On balance it is true to say that the trade takes more money from speculators, especially at times when it is most needed, than speculators take out of the markets in the form of profits. It is only when the market is artificially distorted by excessive speculation that harm can be done. Over the years the Exchange has learnt to cope with the threat posed by speculators or even by trading companies trying to 'corner' the available supplies and in this way to force up the price. Any sign of this happening is quickly spotted and dealt with by the Metal Exchange management committee, which has the ultimate sanction of withdrawing ring-dealing privileges from any company involved.

It is the trust and confidence built up over the past hundred years that gives the Metal Exchange a good reputation throughout the world even if many producers and consumers neither care for the pricing system imposed on them nor for the method by which prices are decided.

The Exchange was founded by a group of merchants and traders in London during the 1870s. It formalized previous informal trading sessions where protection was sought against price fluctuations by forward dealings, which included simply trading in metals. At first one of the members simply drew a large chalk 'ring' on the floor around which other traders gathered to shout out the prices and quantities of metals that they wanted to buy or to sell. Since then a ring of wooden benches with 40 seats for the ring-dealing member companies has replaced the chalk circle. The open cry trading system is used. Dealers shout across the ring during trading sessions the prices at which they wish to buy or sell, and the quantity involved. Deals are struck across the ring between the individual traders, whose clerks take down details for the contracts later required and also keep the company office fully informed of what is happening. This information is then swiftly flashed by modern communication methods throughout the world.

The Exchange has formal trading sessions for the metals traded, spaced out through the day. This enables deals made across the ring to be completed and clients to be kept informed of what is happening so that they can give fresh buying or selling orders before the next trading session starts. In fact the official trading sessions on the ring are confined to the morning. The all-important settlement price, on which many supply contracts are based, is the selling price of cash metal at the end of the morning trading sessions. This is to enable the settlement price to be notified to customers internationally in time for the next day's trading session when they might want to take some further action.

Trading then resumes on an unofficial basis in the afternoon, although under the same rules and regulations. The afternoon session coincides with the start of trading in the United States, which as explained earlier can have a considerable influence on prices. In addition to the trading sessions for the individual metals, there are also kerb trading sessions covering all the metals traded. The term 'kerb' dates back to the time when some members, not wishing to participate in the ring trading, held separate dealings on the kerb outside the Exchange. In fact nowadays trading goes on all the time in inter-office dealings between members and their wide network of customers throughout the world. The trading sessions crystallize the inter-office dealings and provide an opportunity to mirror the mood of market sentiment and trends. The good dealer can save or make considerable sums of money for his customers and company by the speed and astuteness with which he handles trading across the ring.

Ring-dealing membership of the Exchange is not easy to obtain. Seats cannot be bought and sold as they are on other Exchanges, since membership of the Exchange is by election only and each company has to apply for re-election annually. A company wishing to become a ring-dealing member has to be able to prove that it can meet the financial commitments entailed, which can be massive, and the Exchange is insistent that the company must be involved in the metals industry rather than simply dealing as brokers on behalf of clients. Election is by secret ballot. In recent years the Exchange has insisted that companies owned by the same parent group should only have one seat on the ring even if they operate independently. They also insist that there must be a majority shareholder bearing the main financial commitment in any consortium formed to create a dealing company. For much the same reason, any ring-dealing member must be based in London, although this does not preclude overseas companies forming a London subsidiary. The rule that any ring-dealing company should be housed within a mile of the Exchange has been relaxed, although it is a great advantage since each morning, before the Exchange opens for trading, representatives of the member companies sort out details of the previous day's trading and exchange warrants. The building at Whittington Avenue, soon to be transferred to Plantation House, is owned by the Metal Market Exchange Company and its Board is responsible for providing the secretariat required to handle the paperwork and ensure that the right facilities for trading are provided.

But the day-to-day running of the market is in the hands of a Management Committee elected from the membership of the Exchange on an annual basis. This committee in turn elects a chairman and vice-chairman. The functions of the management committee and the Board do overlap but the committee's area of responsibility includes trading rules, regulations and policy. This two-tier structure dates back to a dispute

in the early days of the Exchange when the Board at the time tried to
impose trading regulations which were opposed by a majority of the
membership. They then formed the management committee to take
over this part of the running of the Exchange. Special sub-committees
are formed to deal with specific matters, often in consultation with the
Board.

The 'principals only' system

Another unique feature of the London Metal Exchange is that it has a
principals only system. Other commodity futures markets have a
central clearing or settlement house through which all transactions are
channelled and which takes all the financial risks on behalf of its members. In London the International Commodities Clearing House, a
subsidiary of the finance company United Dominions Trust, provides
the clearing house for most of the non-metal (soft) commodity futures
markets. In the United States the exchanges in New York and Chicago
prefer the settlement house system, which is owned by members of
the market who thereby spread any financial risk amongst many
companies.

On the Metal Exchange each of the ring-dealing members acts as
principal to any transaction. Trading is not with the Metal Exchange
or with a clearing house but with the individual company using a
standard contract which complies with rules and regulations laid down
by the Metal Exchange. There is also an arbitration procedure in the
event of any dispute. This means that each company has to bear the full
financial risk on each transaction and, with the growth in trading and
the rise in the value of metals, the sums at risk are enormous. Traders
attempt to keep a balanced 'book', that is with purchases and sales
matched, but this is no real protection against defaulting since both
transactions can be at risk: either the purchaser fails to pay what is
due or the seller fails to deliver the metal paid for or committed to
delivery elsewhere. There is a compensation fund, made up of contributions from the ring-dealing member companies which covers losses
that might occur in trading between members. It does not cover any
losses that might be sustained by non-members who have to channel
their business through a ring-dealing company in order to trade on the
Exchange. The compensation fund would not be large enough to cope,
even in a limited way, with any sizeable disaster; nor would the cash
and bank guarantees put up by ring-dealing members when they are
elected to membership.

The 'clearing house' system

There are sharply divided views on the Exchange about the introduction of a clearing house system. Some favour it, others claim that it would change the whole unique concept of the market. With a principals' contract the individual companies can decide the scale of deposits and financial guarantees they require from their clients wishing to do business. Since they do not have to provide deposits to a central clearing house, the ring-dealing members can afford to encourage trade by lowering the deposits they require or indeed by not asking for any deposit provided the customer is financially sound and not over-committed. In other instances, notably with speculative clients, the amount required as a deposit on forward transactions is normally at least 10 per cent of the total outlay and sometimes considerably more, if the client is thought to be financially unreliable or if the market is particularly volatile.

Dealing ahead

At the same time the principals' contract is linked with another unique feature of the London Metal Exchange: the fact that it is possible to trade on any business day up to three months ahead on the Exchange and considerably further ahead with individual members. The official quotations on the Exchange only extend up to three months ahead, unlike other futures contracts where trading is possible in the specified delivery months a year ahead or in some cases up to three years ahead. The three months period on the Exchange dates back to the time when it took that time for copper and Straits tin to reach London from Chile and Malaya respectively.

It has not been extended because of the cost involved in members granting credit over a longer period plus the fact that it would be difficult to extend the daily delivery dates, which are much appreciated by trade customers, for longer than three months. However, there is no difficulty in dealing further ahead with any ring-dealing member. The current quotation is simply added to the interest rate involved in carrying the metal required for a longer period and a forward price is calculated.

Under pressure from the Bank of England the Metal Exchange decided in 1978 to proceed with plans for a monitoring system, aimed at giving a much clearer picture of the individual member companies' commitments. This acts as an early warning system allowing for action to be taken if a dangerous situation appears to be building up. The guarantee sums required are adjusted according to the volume of business and the risk undertaken by each member company. Each member company has a credit 'ceiling' which must not be exceeded without putting up further guarantees.

Copper and Tin

Copper is by far the most important market on the Metal Exchange, which is often described as the London Copper Exchange. It has more trading sessions, since there are separate sessions for wirebars and cathodes — the two contracts that have finally evolved. But tin has also been traded on the Exchange since its inception, although obviously in a lower volume as it is far less plentiful than copper. Since the advent of the International Tin Agreement which followed on previous attempts to control the market, the Metal Exchange has played a less important role in influencing tin prices. This role diminished still further when the International Tin Council decided to base its buffer stock ranges on the Straits tin price quoted on the Penang market in Malaysia because of the float of sterling in 1972.

In Britain the collapse of the Williams Harvey smelter in 1973, which had been a major source of tin supplies to the Metal Exchange, brought a further loss of influence, despite the introduction of a new high-grade contract which is geared to allow for trading in the bulk of tin supplies throughout the world. At the time of writing, in 1980, the Metal Exchange market was the only hedging medium available for tin traders throughout the world and thus still plays an important though diminished role. It may be argued that with the International Tin Agreement controlling prices there is less need for hedging facilities but this is not the case. The range in which tin prices can, and do, move under the Agreement is wide enough to create severe losses for the trader mis-calculating the trend in prices. In some ways the Tin Agreement acts as a destabilizing influence since the limits set out under the Agreement provide a target for speculators, both trade and private, to shoot at in the knowledge that specific action will be triggered off — often providing the opportunity for making profits.

At the same time, although the floor price of the Agreement has rarely been breached, there is still only a partial defence against prices going through the ceiling in times of shortage and the buffer stock losing control of the market. Indeed this is recognized, somewhat unfairly, in the Tin Agreement, in that while the buffer stock resources are used to defend the floor price, the sale takes place at the market price, possibly above the ceiling when the top limit is breached. At the same time the dependence of Europe and the LME warehouses on supplies shipped from some distance away means that there is far greater vulnerability to supply 'squeezes' through the dislocation of deliveries.

The amount of tin produced in the main industrialized countries is limited, with the production of the actual tin metal centred around the areas of the mine output of concentrates. This is different from copper, lead and zinc, where a large proportion of the metal is produced in the consuming countries.

The most important physical market for tin is in Penang, where the world's two major tin smelting companies offer their production on a daily basis against bids from buyers. The offers are based on the intake of concentrates from the mines by the smelters. Each day the smelters compile a list of bids received against the supplies available. Starting from the highest bid they work down until supplies for that day are exhausted and the final price is the price for the day. Many traders, of course, hedge their Penang purchases on the London Metal Exchange and there is a close link between the two markets.

In 1977 the Malaysian Government commissioned a study on the prospects for starting a tin futures market, for forward dealing, to operate in conjunction with the Penang physical market. It is part of an overall policy to retain in Malaysia some of the control and profits resulting from futures trading in tin and several other of its main commodity exports. It can be expected, however, that the Metal Exchange market, with its long history and expertise, will retain its important role, especially since it is centred in a consuming area and not as subject to producer influences.

Lead and Zinc

The Metal Exchange lead and zinc markets do not have a long history. They were introduced for the first time in 1920 and, like the other markets, were closed during the Second World War and reopened only in 1953.

The lead market is very similar to copper, except that it operates on a smaller scale and is far less active, thus reflecting the difference between the two metals. Lead has a history of relative price stability since its consumption tends to grow slowly and steadily unlike the violent changes from boom to bust in other metals. A dampening influence on market price movements is the fact that its major outlet, in lead-acid batteries, generates a large proportion of new supplies in the form of recovered scrap. Secondary or recovered lead can be refined back into virtually the same quality as primary lead, and there are few uses that require top purity lead. In Britain and other industrialized countries, where the system for recovery of lead, especially from batteries, has reached a high degree of efficiency, as much as 60 per cent of total supplies comes from scrap sources. The comparable figure for copper is some 40 per cent and it is far less for most other metals, with the exception of aluminium.

There have been occasions when lead prices have shot up as a result of a sudden surge in demand, or more often as a result of the dislocation of supplies in the main producing areas in North America and Australia. But the flow of scrap supplies usually can be rapidly increased given sufficient price incentive.

As with copper, the bulk of lead is sold to consumers under supply contracts with producers, using the Metal Exchange quotations as the basis for the price paid. The Metal Exchange provides the basis for costs of concentrates and ores bought by smelters, as well as for scrap supplies and manufactured metal. It is also an important alternative source of physical supplies, again, like copper, acting as a residual market of last resort.

Lead producers, who are mainly centred in developed countries, have attempted, over the years, to influence the Metal Exchange prices to avoid the kind of fluctuations encountered in copper. Since lead is a smaller market, it is far easier and less costly to undertake support-buying operations. The purchase of a relatively small quantity of lead on the Exchange can be more than justified if, as a result, the price of the bulk of lead sold under supply contracts direct to consumers is increased. Generally the producers' aim is to lift prices, or at least to prevent them from falling. On occasions the selling of surplus metal is used to stop too violent a rise in price which it is feared might hit consumption. However, despite the smaller scale of operations needed to control the market, on occasions producers find it impossible to withstand normal market forces pushing prices down.

These downward pressures were naturally at their strongest during times of surplus supplies, when producing companies were at their weakest with sales falling and their own stocks building up. The cost of carrying extra supplies, acquired under support-buying operations from the Metal Exchange, put producers under a severe financial strain. The alternatives were to bow to pressure and allow prices to fall or to be stuck with surplus stocks acquired at a higher price. The large percentage of scrap supplies in the market, from suppliers with totally different interests and cost structures from primary producers, was a flaw in the whole conception. But the break-up of combined operations by a group of leading producers sharing the cost came when the United States and other governments showed their hostility to this kind of cooperative action, which, it was claimed, ran counter to anti-cartel legislation. The United States Government had a particular interest since the price charged by domestic producers under the producer price system has generally to be aligned with the level of prices in Europe and elsewhere, allowing for shipping costs and the import duty imposed as a protection for US producers. At the same time the main sources of lead production are North America and Australia, where anti-trust legislation has been vigorously enforced. Producers became increasingly nervous about the support-buying operations as it became clear that many companies could not cooperate for fear of being charged with anti-trust activities. In addition, the cost of trying to arrest the general decline in prices during the economic recession became prohibitive.

Support-buying operations were therefore suspended, probably indefinitely. This did not include individual producers, although their existence has never been officially acknowledged.

Similar problems faced the zinc producers' group that in 1964 decided to abandon the use of the Metal Exchange quotations as a pricing basis for supply contracts. Instead, they instituted what is known as the European producer price, used as the basis for contracts throughout the world outside North America which has its own producer price system. In order to maintain the European producer price support-buying operations were needed to take up surplus supplies on the London Metal Exchange, when prices had been driven down to a level which might tempt consumers away from producer supplies to the cheaper LME zinc. This was not a particularly difficult operation since the supplies available to the Metal Exchange zinc market were limited mainly to shipments from communist bloc countries, notably North Korea. Only in times of gross surplus could the Metal Exchange rely on adequate supplies being available, as a result of reselling by consumers, or from producers desperate to sell their surplus zinc. Merchant interest in zinc declined as a result of the producers' grip on the market and trading activity in the free market followed suit with only occasional bursts of interest. The weakness of the LME zinc market was starkly revealed in 1973 when a shortage of available supplies forced the cash price up to an unprecedented £950 per ton — about three times the producer price at the time — and the Metal Exchange had to suspend the selling of cash metal for a period, until more normal conditions were restored.

The European zinc producer price is, in theory, easier to sustain than the producer price for copper and lead, since there is no comparable competitive pressure from scrap supplies. Control of production is centred in relatively few hands, mainly in developed countries, where producers are better able to adjust production in accordance with the changing demand. These producers normally have the facility and financial resources to cut output when necessary, unlike copper producers in developing countries, who cannot afford either the loss of export earnings or the social problems created by increased unemployment.

In fact, the European zinc price, instituted on the initiative of the giant Rio Tinto Zinc group and strongly backed by Belgian and French producers, established itself successfully and worked to the satisfaction of both producers and consumers for over 10 years, with occasional slight hiccups. Meetings between producers were always held unofficially, but decisions on production cutbacks and price increases were quickly made known. Nowadays producers using producer price systems prefer to use a follow-my-leader approach. One company raises or cuts its producer price, other producers decide individually whether they should follow or not, and a general consensus emerges.

However, moves for the stricter enforcement of anti-trust legislation coincided with a period when the support-buying operation was facing a crisis as a result of a slump in demand. This created massive surplus stocks. Producers were in disarray, fearful of meeting together even unofficially, and having to cope with heavy extra costs to finance stocks at unprecedentedly high levels.

The producer price, which had been quoted in sterling, changed to US dollars at the end of 1974. It had been held too high for too long and was heavily discounted by producers and smelters battling for a share of declining sales. Eventually pressure from smelters forced a reduction in the producer price from $795 to $550 a ton in less than two years. An underlying problem for the zinc producers is that smelters, not owned by the mining companies, have a similar attitude to scrap refiners. They are most interested in the difference between the price at which they buy their raw material intake of ore concentrates and the price they can obtain for the refined metal, which represents their profit margin.

This conflict between the interests of mining producers, many of whom also own zinc smelting plants, and the independent European smelters is a constant threat to the European zinc producer price structure. It has continued to exist only because the stability is favoured by consumers and is used as the basis for trading in ore concentrates worldwide. Canadian producers, who provide the bulk of the world's zinc exports, are keen supporters of the producer price system. The big cutback in US zinc refining capacity in the late 1960s which was encouraged by environmental problems now means that the United States has become a large net importer. US buyers historically favour a producer price system. Import competition, however, means that US domestic prices and international prices are even more closely linked than in the past.

The Metal Exchange market, handicapped by the lack of a reliable, regular source of supply, faces a difficult task in operating effectively. The serious blows suffered by the European producer price system have established the Exchange market in a much more influential role in setting price trends. A zinc futures contract was established on the New York commodity exchange in 1978 to cater for the increased flow of imported supplies. The initial reaction to this, as with the reaction to other base metal markets in the United States, with the exception of the Comex copper market, was not encouraging.

Speculation

Speculation, or non-trade investment in metals, has become of increasing importance in the metal markets during the last 10 years. It probably reached its height during the second half of 1979 and the first quarter of 1980 with the well publicised attempt by Texas billionaire, Nelson Bunker Hunt, his family and associates, to 'corner' the world silver market by buying up a large proportion of available supplies.

Mr Bunker Hunt received at least a temporary setback when prices collapsed in early 1980, leaving him, and many other speculators, with heavy losses.

Although the great silver crisis, as it became known, received extensive publicity, it was, in fact, only one in a series of such attempts. Over the years many ambitious speculators have made efforts to win control of different metal markets and the 'silver crisis' is unlikely to be the last such attempt.

The only consolation from the metal traders' point of view is that these attempts have always failed, even if, for a time, they have appeared successful. It is not too difficult to 'corner' a market at certain times, provided the financial resources are available. What has proved impossible so far is to dispose of the metal successfully at the highly inflated price. Once the market starts to fall buyers quickly melt away and the price collapses. In the case of silver the fall was particularly dramatic, from a peak of over £21 ($50) to below £5 per troy ounce in the space of two months.

However, the scale of the silver price fall basically emphasized that the money involved was a much larger amount than ever before. The fear is that an even larger speculator, such as a consortium of oil-rich governments, might decide that it was worthwhile to gain control of certain markets in respect of metals of strategic or political importance, thus creating even more price distortions in the years ahead. There is also the real threat of producer cartels, similar to that formed by oil-producing countries. However, traders are confident that in the long run, even with oil, the basic fundamental laws of supply and demand will reassert themselves and restore market prices to realistic levels. Nevertheless there could be considerable disruption in the interim, and there is no doubt that speculation — and long-term investments — will continue to be an important influence in the metal markets.

There are several reasons for the huge growth of speculative and investment interest in metals and there are many different types of speculators or investors.

For a start there are governments or companies and individuals who decide to buy up one or several metals because they believe that, in the future, supplies will become scarce or exhausted. Metals are, in theory, a finite non-renewable resource being used up at an accelerating rate by a world busily improving its living standards. In fact, there are sufficient reserves deeper in the earth's crust, and in the ocean beds, to last for a long time. But some metals may become more and more difficult to obtain.

On a more practical basis many governments are worried that supplies of certain strategic metals may become scarce as a result of political developments. The most common example quoted is the possibility of a political upheaval in South Africa, which is a key supplier of several important industrial and precious metals. Another cause for alarm, contributing to the the decision to create stockpiles, was provided by the invasion of the Shaba Province in Zaire during 1978 that threatened mines producing nearly 70 per cent of the world's output of cobalt — currently a key metal for jet engines and other strategic manufactures.

There are several other examples of specialist metals, including tin, where production is concentrated in one or two countries or areas, thus making them vulnerable to producer cartels or political disruptions.

Several countries — France, West Germany, Japan and Britain — have already decided to build up stockpiles of certain metals that could be in short supply in the future. The United States too has reviewed its strategic stockpile objectives, basing them on supplies required during a three-year conventional war.

Many of the US stockpile holdings of metals are well below target and will have to be built up, although, ironically, the holdings of tin are deemed to be in considerable surplus. Revenue obtained from sales of tin and silver will, in fact, be used to buy up supplies of other metals and raw materials in deficit.

The fact that these are government stockpiles does not make them different from commercial or private investors who also buy up metals in anticipation of a shortage of supply or a likely price rise. It can, of course, be argued that it is not speculation for a company to buy up metals it requires for manufacturing processes or against future delivery commitments, as a defensive measure in case of a scarcity developing. Indeed, it could be more of a speculation not to take this kind of defensive measure, even though it involves the cost of storage and financing. However, for private investors, taking a long-term view that a certain metal will go up in price, it is a different matter. Much depends on whether the purchase is made with a view to taking advantage of a particular situation in a particular metal or simply as a long-term 'hedge' against the depreciating value of paper money as a result of inflation and currency changes.

It is the fear of the depreciating value of the dollar, in particular, that has encouraged the movement of speculative funds into raw materials, especially metals, which have an intrinsic value. It is argued that raw materials must in the long run reflect the cost of production which in turn takes in all inflationary influences. This is essentially a long-term view but it has been sufficiently important to persuade a growing number of investors and speculators to devote at least a proportion of their investment portfolios to raw materials.

Metals are particularly popular since they are easy to store, do not normally deteriorate in quality and are tangible. They can be held and possessed. The favourites for this kind of speculation or investment are traditionally the precious metals — gold, silver and platinum — which are easily transportable and cashable, retaining their value all over the world in any circumstances.

In times of monetary or political uncertainties there is normally an upsurge of buying interest, even though gold, in particular, has little use as an industrial metal. In recent years speculators have been increasingly looking for alternative safeguards for their money and have turned to other metals, notably copper, where there are big futures markets and publicly quoted prices.

Some speculators have gone even further and started looking seriously at specialist so-called 'minor' metals which, broadly defined, mean metals for which there are no futures markets. In such cases, for example cobalt, speculation is mainly confined to merchants buying and selling the actual metal, since very often large sums have to be expended to take actual delivery rather than buying forward on paper, as in the futures markets, and selling out before the delivery date falls due. But some big private speculators are realising the potential of minor metals and taking advantage of special situations. It does, however, require a long purse and quite often a lot of patience.

The bulk of speculation in metals comes through the futures markets, based in London, New York and Chicago.

Speculators in futures normally only have to put up a deposit or margin, equivalent to about 10 per cent of the total value of the transaction, although this might have to be topped up at times if losses are suffered. The speculator usually has no intention of taking delivery of the metal bought for delivery at some date in the future, be it one month or 12 months ahead. There is therefore no question of becoming involved in storage, finance and insurance costs. A purchase contract is sold out before the delivery date falls due. However, an ominous trend in the silver crisis was that Bunker Hunt and his associates were taking delivery of massive quantities of silver, thereby disrupting the mechanism of the futures markets which are fundamentally designed for 'paper' contracts only. They are not primarily intended to be a source of actual metals, so the taking off the market of large quantities of silver distorted prices by reducing the amount of supplies available.

In other words, 'cornering' the market. The 'corner' proved too expensive to maintain but revealed a flaw in the futures mechanism which is essentially designed for 'paper' transactions alone.

That is certainly the case with the United States futures markets for copper, gold, platinum and silver, where it is possible to trade over a year forward. However, the London Metal Exchange is an exception. Its contracts are for only three months ahead and it is an important market of last resort through which residual supplies pass — those not covered by direct contracts between producers and consumers. These have an important effect on prices.

As mentioned, there are a number of different kinds of speculator, apart from long-term investors. There are trade speculators — companies in the metals industry either as merchants, brokers, producers or consumers who take a position on their own account in addition to any trade hedging they might do. They might well decide market prices have gone too high or too low and seek to take advantage of the supposed imbalance. They also undertake arbitrage trading — buying in one market and simultaneously selling in another to take advantage of any temporary price differentials. Trade speculation accounts for a large proportion of speculative turnover.

A growing development, especially in the United States, is the professional speculator who makes a living simply by buying and selling in the commodity futures markets, including metals. Those speculators provide a large proportion of turnover and add greatly to the liquidity of markets, thus serving a useful function.

It is argued that speculative funds are essential to the market and supply the volume of trading to allow the trade to undertake legitimate 'hedging' operations successfully. If the market is too thin it can be distorted and not properly reflect the trend in physical metals.

Finally there are the outside speculators — either private individuals or non-metal companies — who have shown a growing interest in commodity and metal futures in recent years. This has been the big growth area, following the uncertainties created by the collapse of the Bretton Woods system for currencies and the development of rampant inflation in the industrialized countries.

Speculation in metals was until quite recently considered to be something only for the professionals, the trade, or someone who had more money than sense, since it was viewed as far more risky and expensive than stocks or shares as it yields no dividends or interest.

But that attitude has changed radically, as shown by the great gold and silver boom in late 1979 and the enormous general increase in speculative activity in the metal markets during the years.

Speculation can still be risky and expensive, but it is now on occasions favoured by even the most cautious of investors, especially during times of monetary and political uncertainty. The smaller speculator has been encouraged to enter the markets by various kinds of schemes such as managed funds and syndicates, or options, requiring only a limited amount of money. Thus the number of speculators dealing in the metal markets has increased enormously. There has also been a dramatic rise in the volume of speculation, with private individuals like Bunker Hunt and big financial groups and companies viewing commodity speculation as simply another area of investment on a par with stocks, shares or property.

Each kind of speculation has its own advantages and disadvantages depending on times and circumstances and, in recent years, it has been found that investment in metals yields a more than competitive return in 'real' terms. The leverage in the futures markets, obtained by having to put up only a 10 per cent margin, is extremely attractive in the battle to beat inflation.

It is virtually impossible to say how much outside speculation there is in the metal markets; it varies greatly according to the state of the market. Speculators are mainly attracted by a booming market, hoping for the opportunity of buying cheap and selling back at a far higher price later. They tend to withdraw when prices are sluggish, since there are normally fewer opportunities for making short-term profits in dull conditions. This means that there is a considerable variation in the volume of speculation from time to time and from market to market. There is also the vexed question of how speculation is defined. If it is prudent and sensible to buy a metal if it is feared that a shortage will develop and endanger the supplies needed to keep a factory going, then it must also be wise to protect one's funds against the depreciating value of money. Therefore this is not necessarily speculation but a wise precaution. The problem is that many investors tend to rush into metals for protection against possible currency changes or through fears of inflation at a time when the metal is already over-priced and well above its cost of production. This provides little or no protection; indeed it might involve heavy losses. Buying silver at £5 an ounce in mid-1979 as a hedge against inflation was one thing — a justifiable investment; buying it at £21 six months later would be viewed as a very foolish speculation.

So the amount of speculation in a market can vary greatly from virtually zero to a very large percentage of total turnover. However, it is generally agreed that the United States futures markets in New York and Chicago rely to a far greater extent on speculative activity than does the London Metal Exchange. This is largely to do with the different structures of the Exchanges. In the United States a considerable proportion of market members are independent, professional speculators who make their living by dealing on the market all day. They have to trade a lot and encourage price fluctuations in order to justify the cost of membership. And they take advantage of any developments or news to move the market either up or down. There are also a large number of outside speculators in the United States with massive funds at their disposal, who, over the years, have become used to dealing in commodities, just as they do in stocks and shares. The United States metal futures markets are largely designed for these speculators, since until recently domestic metal producers in the US sold the bulk of their supplies at a fixed producer price and, to a large extent, ignored the fluctuations in New York or London. Subsequently, with the increased US dependence on imports for metal supplies, they have been forced to change the pricing system but the structure of the markets has not changed.

In London the structure is different: the markets on the Metal Exchange were created and designed for the trade, particularly the merchants who dominated the City of London at one stage. The nature of the contract, the quotations only three months ahead but dealings permitted on a day-to-day basis, rather than monthly, is intended for the benefit of the trade. Special terms are offered, with many big companies in the trade not even having to put up margins for their dealings. In the main, speculation is an unpopular word on the London Metal Exchange, whereas in the United States this is certainly not the case. However, the situation is changing in line with the changing attitudes in the world. Speculators have now moved into the London markets, despite some of the disadvantages. This trend is expected to accelerate as the US markets become subject to stricter controls and regulations. Already the daily limit on price movements, used in the US markets as a protective measure for speculators and dealers, has proved somewhat unpopular and driven business to London. However, it is obvious that if London and United States prices are to stay roughly in line, as they must do because of arbitraging between the markets, then the large volume of speculation in the United States must have a tremendous impact on London. If, for example, the price of copper in New York is forced up to the equivalent of £2,000 a ton by heavy speculative buying, it would be impossible for it to remain at £1,500 in London, unless there was sufficient selling pressure which would then bring the New York price down to £1,500. Therefore, when there is a market imbalance and free trade is permitted, it is clear that the buying pressure would go to the cheapest market and the sellers to the more expensive prices, and the two would quickly come into line.

It is also true to say that London by itself is attracting far more speculative business direct, as the popularity of speculation in the markets has grown in Europe, and other areas in a similar time zone to London. The metals trade likes to claim that in the long run the fundamental supply and demand position of the metal will always assert itself, whatever the speculator might do. Indeed, it is said that speculation really helps to smooth out prices by coming in when the market is depressed and the trade disinterested; speculators often acting as sellers when prices have been forced artificially high by strong trade demand.

Trade demand tends to be influenced by the same factors — a boom or depression in the economy — whereas speculative activity reflects a quite different motive, the making of profits. So very often, when the trade is moving in one direction, either buying or selling, the speculator is quite happy to provide the obverse side to the market if it is thought profitable to do so. However, it must also be said that speculators are often blamed for exaggerating price trends, by jumping on the buying bandwagon when a shortage is developing; or selling, when the outlook for trade demand is worsening. The influence of speculators can be profound when a market is delicately balanced with either a small surplus of supplies or a minor shortage. The resultant sharp price movement in one direction or the other, triggered off by speculative activity, may then lead to the supply/demand balance being restored more quickly than might otherwise have been the case. But the temporary fluctuation in the price can be very harmful if overdone. So far speculation has been kept under reasonable control for most of the time, although on occasions in the past there has been some cause for concern. There are renewed fears now, with the example of the Bunker Hunt silver crisis in mind, that the growth of interest in commodity and metal market speculation could bring more serious problems in the future, especially in the specialist metals markets that might prove extremely vulnerable.

Part 2:
The Metals

Aluminium

Aluminium metal production, 1978   *million metric tons*

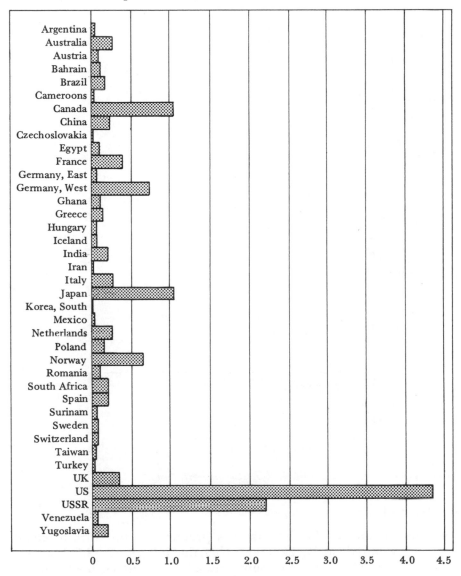

Total world production 14,531,600 metric tons

Aluminium metal consumption, 1978 *million metric tons*

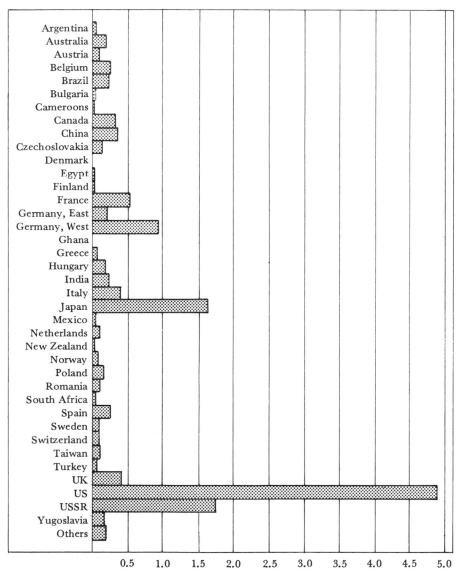

Total world consumption 14,707,400 metric tons

Grades available

The bulk of unwrought aluminium is produced in the form of ingots weighing approximately 22 kilos with the purity of 99.5 per cent minimum or 99.7 per cent minimum. Many smelters, however, can offer a large range of shapes and grades, including 'T' bars — up to 1000 kilos each; sows, 200-500 kilos each; extrusion billets; rolling slabs and wire rods.

Most modern smelters are designed to produce metal with the minimum purity of 99.7 per cent with iron content below 0.2 per cent and the silicon content below 0.1 per cent.

Production method

Aluminium is the most abundant metallic element in the earth's crust. The metal is extracted from alumina (aluminium oxide) which is produced from bauxite, a naturally occurring ore.

It is produced by the electrolysis of alumina with cryolite, a natural mineral that can also be made synthetically. The anode of the electrolytic production cell is made of carbon which combines with the oxygen in the alumina when the current is passed through and sufficient heat is generated, reducing the alumina to the metal. The molten metal is then cast into the moulds required.

Major uses

More aluminium is produced than any other non-ferrous metal, and none has such a diverse range of uses. The metal has a high thermal and electrical conductivity and a high strength, particularly when alloyed with small quantities of other metals such as silicon and manganese. It is extremely ductile and has found many uses as sheet and foil, and can be cast comparatively easily into all kinds of complex shapes.

Its resistance to corrosion and its attractive appearance makes this metal suitable for many applications in the construction industry. Its lightness (aluminium is less than half as heavy as steel) makes it the most important metal in the aircraft industry. The versatility of aluminium explains its phenomenal growth rate.

It competes with copper in its application as a conductor of electricity, with steel in construction, with zinc for castings and with stainless steel in its corrosion free properties. It is also used for 'deoxidizing', that is the property of removing oxygen from molten iron and steel. There are few manufacturing and industrial activities which do not have a substantial use for this most useful of metals.

Main market features

Because of the economic and political instability of some of the main bauxite producing countries, many aluminium manufacturers are investigating the possibility of producing the metal from other minerals containing aluminium, of which there are many. These include china clay and shales, and good progress is being made in this field. These efforts, however, have been interpreted as a deterrent to any potential threat from major bauxite exporters who might wish to form a cartel to force price increases.

It has become almost fashionable of late for an emerging nation to attach great priority to the building of its own aluminium smelters. This is particularly true of countries in the Middle East, South America and South East Asia. The pattern usually includes the majority share-holding held by the country concerned with a minority interest held by a large aluminium producing company which provides all the technical expertise to construct and run the smelter.

The recent history of the industry has been marked by the failure of the market to predict future consumption trends. This has resulted in a large degree of over-capacity in times of stagnant demand, and shortages in times of high demand. The phenomenom is partly due to the long period (about five years) from the date of conception of a new production plant, to the date of commencement of production.

Predictions of the aluminium consumption growth rate vary from 4-8 per cent per annum over the next decade, a very high growth rate for a metal, whichever forecast is used. It should be remembered that, although the price per metric ton of aluminium may seem close to the price of any one of its competitors, the lightness of the metal means that one metric ton will go much further: it has greater volume than any of its competitors, with the exception of magnesium.

Aluminium is essential in the manufacture of highly sophisticated items such as computers and aircraft, but is also used for making commonplace items such as cooking pots. Its consumption, therefore, is not much affected by technical changes in any industry. The market for aluminium is affected by fundamental factors including the supply of raw material, general world economic activity and competition from other metals.

By and large production is expected to keep pace with consumption but a high factor (about 10-15 per cent) of the cost of production is energy. The ever increasing cost of construction of smelters and of raw materials will inevitably result in an average rise in price. Fluctuations in price from year to year may be more extreme as control of the market shifts from the very few large producers to the many new ones.

Known world reserves (bauxite)

5,842,000,000 metric tons. This is equivalent to 1,168,400,000 metric tons of aluminium metal.

Method of marketing and pricing

The major producers publish an official price for aluminium, the most important of which is the American price. All American producers, at least theoretically, abide by this price. The price is for virgin, unwrought ingots or sows with a minimum purity of 99.5 per cent, CIF major Western ports. There are premiums for a higher purity, different shapes, delivery to works and other ports, or for the delivery of molten metal in specially designed lorries. Most major manufacturers are vertically integrated, producing everything from ingots to foil to manufactured items, often through subsidiaries and associated companies. They are frequently their own largest customers.

Similar official pricing systems exist in the UK, Japan, Continental Europe and other industrialized countries, but in times of glut, producers are often forced to sell at discounts on their official price. These discounts are often hidden in extended payment terms or other similar devices.

There is a growing free market in aluminium, and in October 1978 the London Metal Exchange introduced an aluminium futures contract that has established itself as a pricing and hedging medium despite initial strong opposition from leading producers. However, the Metal Exchange market is not significant for industry as UK producers retain control over prices and marketing. The free market is conducted by international trading houses, which generally have no financial connection with producers. These merchants, however, may have a close working relationship with major smelters and could, for instance, conduct 'location swops' or 'time swops' between producers. That is to say they find one smelter with the stock at point A and the sale at point B and another smelter with the stock at point B and the sale at point A. They simply arrange a swop, thus saving transport costs, and also collect a commission. If you assume A and B to be times, such as March and July, the swop on this basis is a 'time swop', which saves one company's interest costs. The merchant may also arrange tolling contracts, that is to say he may arrange with the smelter to utilize surplus production capacity to convert the merchant's alumina into ingots for a fixed price per metric ton.

The bulk of free market activity is concerned with the trading of metal from small producers who have no fixed pricing policy and insufficient international marketing arrangements. They must sell to merchants at the best possible price, but in times of shortage they have the advantage in that they are able to obtain higher sales prices than the major producers who abide by official price policies.

This merchant activity accounts for about 10 per cent of the world's aluminium trade and the prices recorded for these transactions give the best guide to market trends. Aluminium merchants are active in most major commercial centres of the world.

Scrap and secondary aluminium

Many of the useful aluminium alloys can be made from scrap simply by melting it down, adding other metallic alloying agents and perhaps a percentage of pure aluminium, to produce the right specification. This has ensured a very active scrap market. Indeed, the scrap price may be at times as much as 85 per cent of the pure aluminium price.

World secondary aluminium production is approximately one third of primary production.

Aluminium metal prices   *US cents per lb*

Antimony

Antimony metal production, 1978 *thousand metric tons*

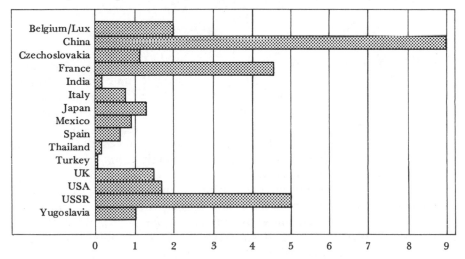

Total world production 32,818 metric tons

Grades available

Antimony metal is normally marketed with the purity between 99 per cent and 99.85 per cent, the most common grades being 99.5 per cent and 99.65 per cent. Particular attention is paid to the arsenic content which most consumers require to be below 0.2 per cent. The normal Chinese grade of 99.65 per cent minimum and 0.15 per cent As maximum has become the most commonly traded grade. The metal is traded in the form of ingots which weigh between 20 and 50 pounds.

Production method

Antimony is produced from its ore, stibnite — antimony sulphide — by roasting to oxide, followed by reduction to the metal by heating with coke in a simple process. Antimony concentrates, derived as a by-product from the production of other metals, mainly lead, are usually in the sulphide form and are dealt with in the same way.

Major uses

By far the largest use for antimony, half its total consumption in fact, is in batteries where it is alloyed with lead. Its effect on lead is to make it more robust and to reduce corrosion by chemicals. The metal is also combined with lead and other metals in the manufacture of solders, print metal, electric cable sheaths, and in certain types of ammunition. Its oxide is particularly important in the manufacture of flame retardant paints and plastics, and as white pigment.

Main market features

China is the largest producer of the metal and has, by far, the largest reserves. Its dominance of the market is having a major effect on large Western producers, particularly in the US and the UK. These producers appear to have decided to concentrate on the production of antimony oxide and the recycling of antimonial lead, mainly from scrap car batteries. Although they still produce a little metal for their domestic customers, they leave this market mainly to the Chinese. Antimony oxide is made directly from the ore, but there have been a few temporary occasions in recent times, when market circumstances have allowed producers to manufacture oxide profitably from the metal.

Antimonial lead is an alloy of between 3 per cent and 10 per cent antimony in lead and is used to make the plates in batteries. A large proportion of this material comes from treatment of used and scrap batteries.

Consumption of antimony by the automobile industry is a dominant feature of this market, not only because of its use in car batteries, but also for its use in flame retardant plastics needed in cars.

There are substitutes for antimony in all its major uses. Other inorganic chemicals are used as flame retardants and these are cheaper and less toxic. However, antimony is still used as a flame retardant in the plastic insulation of electric cables as the bulk required of the alternative flame retardant affects the plastic's mechanical qualities.

Calcium combined with a little tin can and does replace antimony in car batteries and some major car manufacturers are incorporating this feature in new models, in spite of the fact that calcium-lead batteries are more difficult to charge.

Known world reserves

Approximately 3,550,000 metric tons of which 2,000,000 metric tons are estimated to be in China.

Method of marketing and pricing

There is an active free market in antimony metal ore and trioxide but the prices of these three items have little relationship to each other in the short term. The antimony metal market is rather volatile and attracts speculation, mainly from the merchants who deal in it. This feature is reinforced somewhat by the unpredictability of the Chinese marketing policy. Virtually all Chinese production is sold to international merchants who, in turn, distribute to consumers (many of the major consumers in the free market are in Eastern Europe).

Japan, a major consumer of antimony in the form of ore, trioxide and metal, has been producing far less of its own material in recent years and now relies heavily on imported material, especially from China.

Most Western producing countries have high import tariff barriers, but in times of shortage these countries become net importers from China and other producing countries. Periods of shortage are, however, comparatively short-lived. This situation may change as the major

Antimony metal prices (free market)   *US dollars per metric ton*

Western producers become less interested in the metal market. Prices are recorded of deals between the merchants operating in the world's major financial areas, particularly in Europe. The Western producers fix a price for domestic sales, but these official prices are greatly influenced by free market trends and may frequently be adjusted.

Scrap recovery

Very little scrap antimony is traded, but there is a comparatively large market in antimonial lead.

Arsenic

Arsenic (trioxide) approximate production, 1979   *thousand metric tons*

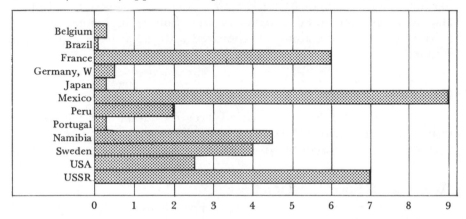

Total world production 36,500 metric tons

Grades available

Elemental arsenic is not strictly a metal in the chemical sense but is referred to as a metal to distinguish it from the oxide in which form it is most commonly distributed. The pure metal is traded in the form of irregularly shaped lumps with a purity of 97 per cent minimum packed in airtight and water-tight drums.

Pure arsenic is rarely traded by merchants but they are a little more active in the arsenic oxide market. The oxide is traded as white powder with a minimum purity of 99 per cent. It is, of course, extremely poisonous and is packed in sealed drums.

Production method

Arsenic is found in many different types of minerals which usually contain other metals particularly lead, copper, zinc, nickel and gold and it is also found together with iron and known as pyrite.

The arsenic is produced from these minerals either as a by-product or co-product of the metal with which it is associated.

In most smelting methods the arsenic is collected as a flue dust in the metal refining process. It is then added to pyrite or galena and heated until the arsenic comes off as a gas which is then collected.

Major uses

About 97 per cent of arsenic production is in the form of oxide which is mainly used to make a large variety of pesticides. Other uses are as a decolourizer in the glass industry and in metal refining.

Pure arsenic is used as an addition to lead in alloys to increase hardness and to copper where it increases corrision resistance. Copper arsenic pipes were used extensively in steam train locomotive fire-boxes but this use has almost disappeared with the passing of the steam train era.

Main market features

Arsenic production is widely spread over the globe and the oxide is rather inexpensive. In the last few years, however, environmental considerations have discouraged production as well as consumption.

Arsenic metal prices (producer price)   *£ per metric ton*

Sweden, traditionally the largest producer, effectively controlled the world's arsenic prices but production in Sweden has now fallen so low that producer prices have become less important over recent years. In this same period production has fallen faster than consumption, which has produced the surprising anomaly of a shortage in this highly toxic material. This situation is not likely to continue, however, as there is no theoretical difficulty in producing arsenic, especially in developing countries where pollution controls are less stringent.

Pure arsenic is much more expensive than the arsenic oxide, but most oxide producers are not interested in producing the elemental form from the oxide. This has led to short periods of active free market trading in times of shortage but demand is somewhat erratic and no sustained period of shortage is possible because so little of the oxide is used to produce the metal.

Method of marketing and pricing

Pure arsenic metal prices are closely controlled by producers but a free market does emerge at premium prices in short periods of high demand. Merchants are only occasionally involved in the oxide market but trade is now highly competitive between producers.

Beryllium

Beryllium ore production (metal content), 1977 *short tons*

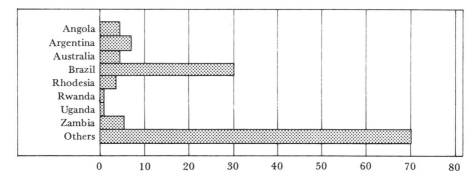

Total world production 125 short tons

Grades available

Pure beryllium metal is rarely traded. Apart from being an extremely toxic metal, which makes handling very dangerous, it is only used commercially in the form of an alloy with other metals. It is therefore safer and easier to market beryllium in the form of a master alloy (an alloy with a high beryllium content compared with its content in the final form) which can then be diluted in the melt. The most common of these master alloys is beryllium-copper with a content of up to 5 per cent beryllium.

Production method

There are several ways of extracting beryllium oxide from its ore, beryl. A common method is to fuse beryl with potassium carbonate. It is then treated with sulphuric acid and the silica is filtered off with water. The liquor containing beryllium is then poured into hot ammonium carbonate and beryllium carbonate is precipitated. When this is redissolved in ammonium carbonate, beryllium oxide is precipitated. The metal is produced from the oxide by reduction in an electric furnace.

Major uses

Most beryllium is used in the form of beryllium-copper, a very important copper alloy used to make marine propellors, springs, aircraft engine components and electrical contacts. It is also used to make non-spark producing tools for use in coal mines and oil refineries, where there is a danger due to inflammable gases. There are minor applications for other beryllium alloys such as beryllium-nickel, and some pure beryllium is used, mainly in nuclear energy plants.

Main market features

Although beryllium ore is produced in many countries, the production of the metal is in very few hands and these are mainly in the US. These producers effectively control the market. This situation is understandable since there are dangers involved in producing the metal due to toxicity and, in addition, the market is small. Producers are rarely asked to supply pure beryllium metal, but conduct most of their business in master alloys.

There is almost no merchant activity in this metal.

Method of marketing and pricing

The main producers have been successful in controlling prices and there is practically no free market outside this system.

Beryllium ore prices *US dollars per short ton unit of BeO*

Bismuth

Bismuth metal production, 1977   *hundred metric tons*

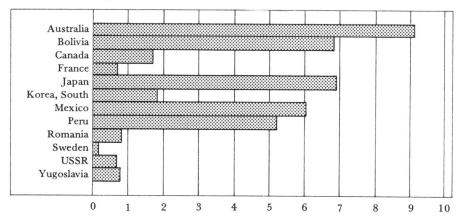

Total world production approx. 4047 metric tons

Grades available

Bismuth is marketed in the form of ingots usually weighing 10 kilos each and packed in wooden boxes each weighing 100 kilos, or in the form of needles or granules weighing between 3 and 5 grams each and packed in 100 kilo steel drums.

Purity is 99.95 per cent minimum up to 99.99 per cent minimum. Some small producers market bismuth in a low refined state (around 96 per cent purity) known as bismuth bullion, usually contaminated with lead. Consumers of the metal who produce pharmaceutical products may demand a low tolerance of trace elements.

Production method

Usually as a by-product of lead or zinc manufacture but also as a by-product of copper, silver, gold and tin refining. The bismuth rich concentrates, usually sulphides, are oxidized in a simple and inexpensive process to the metal. It is then upgraded by skimming and recrystallization and treatment with flucculents to produce metal with a purity of 99.99 per cent suitable for most industrial and pharmaceutical uses.

Major uses

a) *Pharmaceutical* Some salts of bismuth have been found beneficial in the treatment of indigestion and other minor ailments of the alimentary canal and these account for over half the world's consumption. The French, however, who have traditionally consumed almost one third of the world's production for this purpose, decided in 1974 to make bismuth products available to patients only on prescription which has had the effect of reducing that country's consumption by over half. Applications have been found for other bismuth salts in cosmetics.

b) *Fusible Alloys* Bismuth is used as an alloy with lead, cadmium and other metals in the manufacture of fusible alloys, the bulk of which is used as jigs for making parts in the aircraft industry, and also in the manufacture of optical lenses. Other uses are found for these alloys in press moulding machines, the dyeing of textiles, fire sprinkler systems and solders.

c) *Catalysts* Bismuth salts are used in a range of catalysts, particularly in the manufacture of acrylonitrile, a raw material for a man-made fibre.

d) *Alloying agent* Bismuth is added to certain aluminium alloys to improve machinability and also to other metals for specialized uses.

Main market features

Consumption of bismuth has been subject to large fluctuations. The popularity of bismuth as a catalyst in the 1960s and the legislation concerning medical products in France, together with the fortunes and misfortunes of the world's aircraft industry, have all contributed to make the bismuth market one of the world's most volatile. The price volatility itself has contributed to nervousness amongst potential consumers, but bismuth has some unique physical characteristics which must find a continuing interest in industry, especially at its current very low price.

In 1974 France consumed 1,259 metric tons, almost one third of the world's bismuth production. By 1977 consumption in France had fallen to 644 tons and by 1978 to only 346 tons. This fall was a direct consequence of action taken by the French medical authorities to curb the use of bismuth in pharmaceutical products after doubts had been raised concerning side effects suffered by some patients who took bismuth preparations in large doses.

One of the largest bismuth producers in recent years is Australia, where it is produced as a co-product with other metals. It is unlikely that any shortage of bismuth could occur for several years.

There is no official market for bismuth. The major producers fix an official price, but in times of shortage the material is rationed to consumers and the official price is often raised. In times of glut the producers offer discounts on the official price.

It is true to say that since the late 1960s the major producers have lost control of the pricing of this metal and free market forces have taken over. Although perhaps only 25 per cent of the world's production is distributed by merchants, it is their transactions that give the best guide to the price movements.

The merchants who specialize in bismuth, trading mainly in New York, London, Brussels and Dusseldorf, trade the metal throughout the working day, buying surplus stocks from producers and distributing to consumers. These merchants often speculate by holding stocks or 'going short' of the metal and therefore often trade between themselves. They trade in minimum one metric ton lots, but average transactions would be five metric tons.

There is very little scrap trade in bismuth, except for some adulterated alloys that may need extensive refining.

Bismuth metal prices (free market)   *US dollars per lb*

Estimated world reserves
93,000 metric tons.

Cadmium

Cadmium metal production, 1979   *thousand metric tons*

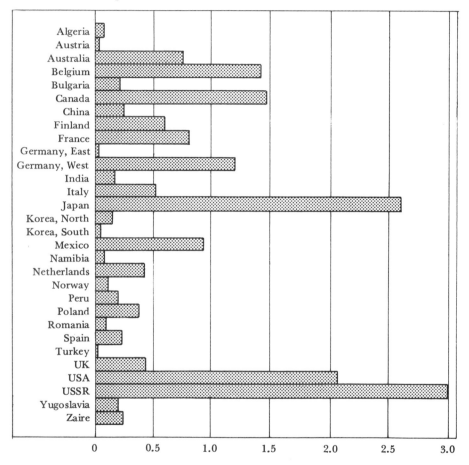

Total world production 18,600 metric tons

Cadmium metal consumption, 1976 *hundred metric tons*

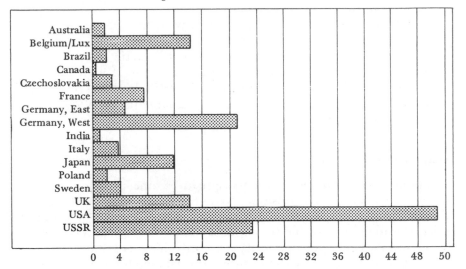

Total world consumption 17,088 metric tons

Grades available

Cadmium is marketed in forms determined by its use: balls approximately 2 ins in diameter for plating, sticks about 10 ins long and ½ in diameter for use in chemical works, and ingots which are used in alloys. Purity is most commonly 99.95 per cent minimum, but often 99.99 per cent minimum which is required for some chemical purposes.

Production method

Almost all cadmium is produced as a by-product of zinc production, but it may also occur in recoverable quantities in lead and copper ores.

Cadmium rich residues are collected in base metal refining processes usually in the form of flue dusts. It is then dissolved in sulphuric acid and the metal is either separated electrolitically or by chemical methods. Further purification can then be carried out by distillation.

Major uses

Cadmium has four major uses — in plating, pigments, polyvinyl chloride stabilizers and in alloys. Plating is the most established use. Cadmium plating of steel products is carried out to ensure a firmer base for another plated metal, like chrome, which would be electroplated over the cadmium to counteract certain corrosive elements, such as sea water. Mechanical and electronic equipment used in coastal or marine work often requires cadmium plating.

Cadmium salts which are made directly from the metal are used to make pigments for ceramics and plastics and are used as stabilizers in the manufacture of PVC. Cadmium is highly toxic and this prevents it being used in any material that comes into contact with foodstuffs.

The metal is also used in combination with tin, lead and other metals to make a variety of solders, print metal and fusible alloys used in sprinkler systems and in fusible jigs.

Main market features

Cadmium production is as widely spread as zinc production and no single producer is in a position to control the market. Like many similar metals the North American producers publish a producers' price for home buyers and for exports. Most other producers, however, don't seem to set a high priority on controlling cadmium prices, and sell at the best price they can to international merchants who specialize in the trading of minor metals.

Cadmium metal prices (free market)   *US dollars per lb*

Known world reserves

Approximately 550,000 metric tons.

Method of marketing and pricing

Cadmium is a favoured trading item for metal merchants who trade on a free market price. The cadmium market is fairly small and very volatile, due to merchant manipulation. The fact that cadmium is a by-product of zinc production means that more metal cannot be produced simply because demand rises.

The market has also attracted the attention of non-trade speculators, which has further distorted the normal rules of supply and demand.

Producers and consumers alike are increasingly concerned with pollution problems associated with cadmium as it is a highly toxic metal. This may tend to reduce activity in this market.

Cerium

Cerium (monazite ore) production, 1975

thousand short tons

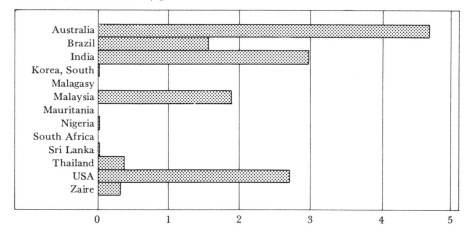

Total world production 11,895 short tons

Grades available

Pure cerium metal is of no interest to the metal dealer and is only produced for laboratory uses and research purposes.

Mischmetal, however, a mixture of rare earth metals containing about 50 per cent cerium, is regularly traded in the form of small ingots, pellets and notched bars.

Production methods

There are several ores containing cerium and other rare earth elements, the most common of which is monazite. It is also found in commercially recoverable quantities in xenatime, bastnaesite and loparite. Monazite is found in a beach sand ore and the rare earths are recovered here as a by-product of titanium production. Rare earth ores are separated from the beach sand by magnetic and electrostatic means. They are concentrated by flotation and the metal (mischmetal) is produced by electrolysis of the rare earth chlorides.

Major uses

Cerium compounds, particularly the oxide, have several important uses as filters and de-colourizers in the glass industry and as catalysts in petrochemical production.

Mischmetal alloyed with iron is used as lighter flints, but its main metallurgical use is as an addition together with magnesium to certain cast irons known as nodularized irons. It is also added to certain types of steels to increase strength and ductility.

Main market features

There are very few companies engaged in the manufacture of cerium products and mischmetal. These companies are mainly in industrialized countries and have enough control of the market to maintain an effective producer price in times of normal demand. There have been a few brief periods in the last two decades when unexpectedly high demand has led to an active free market in mischmetal. During these periods major producers have rationed material to their regular customers. Consumers, especially in the cast iron industry, have then appeared as buyers often at quite substantial premiums to the producer price.

Temporary shortages of mischmetal production have also resulted from inadequate supplies of suitable ore or intermediate raw materials.

The effect of small mischmetal additions to iron and steel is a rather complicated and interesting branch of metallurgy and new uses for this compound are expected to increase demand in this field.

Known world reserves

Cerium containing ores are 10 million tons of rare earth oxide contained, about half of which is estimated to be in the US.

Method of marketing and pricing

As has been mentioned, a few producers of cerium products operate in industrialized countries where they sell direct to consumers, especially on their domestic market, at fixed producer prices. During the comparatively short-lived periods of shortage, however, mischmetal has attracted attention from international merchants operating at premium levels.

Cerium (mischmetal) prices (UK producers prices)   *£ per kilo*

Chromium

Chrome ore production, 1977 *million metric tons*

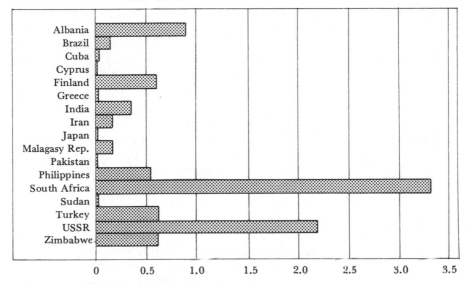

Total world production 9,700,000 metric tons

Grades available

Only a small part of chrome produced is converted into chromium metal. The bulk of chromium is used in the form of its ore (chromite) or ferro-chrome. Chromite ore is simply mined, cleaned, crushed and graded. Ferro-chrome, the alloy of chrome and iron, is produced in several grades. Charge-chrome (containing about 55 per cent chrome), high carbon ferro-chrome (5-8 per cent carbon); and low carbon (0.1 per cent carbon maximum). Of these three, the cheapest is charge-chrome. Another inexpensive chrome containing alloy is ferro-silicon chrome.

Chromite is invariably sold in bulk but ferro-chrome is sold in a lumpy form and may be transported in bulk or packed in steel drums.

Production methods

Chromite is melted in an arc-furnace together with iron to produce ferro-chrome. Chromium metal is produced either by electrolysis of a chromium solution or by alumino thermic reduction, whereby chromium oxide is mixed with aluminium powder and ignited, thus reducing the oxide to chromium metal.

Method of marketing and pricing

World trade in chromium can be confused by the complications of tariff barriers and quota systems in individual markets. However, the price trend is set by South African producers and followed competitively by Russian exports. Very recently the USSR has been a little more erratic in its sales policy and has occasionally withdrawn as sellers to the market. This reflects the general trend of the USSR consuming more of its own metal production. Most business is conducted by producers and their agents but there is an extremely active free market conducted by large merchants utilizing particularly Russian supplies and material from the smaller producing countries. Business is highly competitive mainly because the important trade is conducted with very large steel mills which usually place business on a long-term basis. There are many nationally based merchants who trade on a smaller scale with small specialist steel works and foundries.

Major uses

About 20 per cent of the chromite mined is used directly in refractories, foundry mould sand and other non-metallurgical uses. Its other two major uses are in alloy form in steels and for plating. Chrome is added, in the form of ferro-chrome, to steel to produce alloys including stainless steel. There is a large range of very useful chrome steels but by far the most common of these is normal stainless steel containing both chrome and nickel.

Pure chromium metal is used to manufacture many types of non-ferrous alloys and super alloys, used in magnets amongst other things. Chromium is plated on to such items as automobile trim and cutlery from a bath of chromic acid which is made directly from chromite.

Main market features

Perhaps the most outstanding feature of the chromium market is the fact that the US, the world's biggest end-user of chrome, has no indigenous production.

Chromium is one of the world's most important industrial metals and recent events have once more underlined the potential vulnerability of the US chromium consumer to foreign political events.

South Africa and the USSR produce between them about half the world's chromium in the form of chromite ore and ferro-chrome. Together they represent the bulk of the world's exports.

It can be understood that the US is not too happy about being dependent on either the USSR or South Africa for the supply of such an essential raw material.

Zimbabwe is a major producer of chromium, accounting for some 8 per cent of world production. Much of this material has been exported by various devious means during the period of UN sanctions. The future of that country appears healthy but should a major upheaval occur chrome supply could again be disrupted.

Another important feature of the chrome market is the technical innovation in the production of stainless steel. The comparatively new AOD (Argon-Oxygen Decarburising Vessel) has been found to be the most efficient method of producing stainless steel and among its technical advantages is its ability to utilize lower quality raw materials including chrome.

In the past, ferro-chrome producers were encouraged to reduce the carbon content in their product, an extremely expensive operation. With the advent of the AOD, carbon content can be substantially reduced in the steel making process. Ferro-chrome producers, aware of this change, have swung over on a large scale to the production of charge chrome with a chrome content of about 55 per cent as opposed to the 70 per cent chrome content in standard, medium, and low carbon ferro-chrome. The carbon content of charge chrome

Low carbon ferro-chromium prices *£ per kilo of chromium contained*

can be as high as 6-8 per cent without worrying stainless steel producers using AODs.

Due to the strategic importance of chromium supplies, several Western governments are considering the stockpiling of this metal. The West German Government has already made plans to build up a large stockpile. Purchases will commence in 1980 and may amount to several hundreds of thousands of tons.

Known world reserves

Approximately 775 million metric tons of chromite ore. 575 million metric tons are estimated to be in South Africa.

Cobalt

Cobalt metal production, 1978   *thousand metric tons*

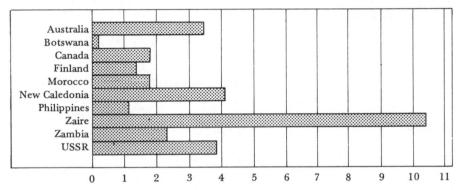

Total world production 30,300 metric tons

Grades available

The most commonly traded form of cobalt is broken cathodes, small flat pieces of the metal produced by crushing a cathode of the brittle pure metal. Granules are a less common form of the pure metal but both are normally distributed with a purity of 99.6 per cent minimum.

Production method

Cobalt is almost universally produced as a by-product, or co-product, of either nickel or copper, except in Morocco where the metal is mined on its own with copper as the by-product. The cobalt rich concentrates are normally collected during the electrolysis of the base metal concerned and is itself produced by electrolysis.

Major uses

The two major uses for this metal are in what is termed super alloys used extensively in the aircraft industry (it is impossible at present to make a modern jet engine without the use of cobalt alloys) and in turbines. Super alloys are usually high alloy steels but may contain only other non-ferrous metals. The second major use is again in alloys, consisting of cobalt and other non-ferrous metals used to make magnets and other electromagnetic components in the electronics industry.

Cobalt alloys are extremely useful in applications where strength at high temperatures is required. There are certain important applications for cobalt salts, particularly the oxide, which is used as a catalyst in the petrochemical industry and as pigment in ceramics and enamels.

There is a very minor use for cobalt isotopes in the treatment of cancer. Pure cobalt powder has an application in sintered products such as machine tools and ammunition when combined with other refractory metals.

Main market features

Many of cobalt's applications are in highly strategic areas, such as its use in aircraft engines and fuselages. It is interesting to note that although the US consumes over one third of the world's production, directly or indirectly, it has almost no production of its own.

Before 1978 Zaire accounted for about 65 per cent of the world's cobalt production. However, in that year Shaba, the important mining province of Zaire, was raided by a rebel army which had the effect of disrupting production for some months and driving away most of the skilled white engineers who worked on cobalt production. This caused cobalt prices to increase by some 600 per cent in a few months and, although prices fell again when production resumed once more, at a reduced output, there is still a shortage of supply.

High prices have stimulated increased production from all the other major producers and stimulated some new mining ventures which may eventually alleviate some of the shortage. Demand has been increasing, however, especially in the booming aircraft industry, so much so that delivery of some aircraft components has been put back due to shortages of cobalt supplies.

Zaire and Zambia (the world's second largest producer) have considerable political and economic difficulties, and the possibility of further supply disruption cannot be ruled out. On the other hand, both countries have a great incentive to produce as much cobalt as possible and have announced plans to increase production considerably.

High prices have encouraged consumers to recycle as much scrap material as possible and to find suitable substitutes. The shortage is expected to last for several years to come, however, especially as both the American and German governments have announced that they will be buying the metal to stockpile.

Known world reserves

Approximately 1,100,000 tons of which 700,000 tons are estimated to be in Zaire.

Method of marketing and pricing

Until the disruption of supplies from Zaire, 90 per cent of all cobalt produced was marketed on a producer price basis. Accelerating prices have encouraged a very active free market, so much so that most producers now have to buy up to 30 per cent of their supplies from free market traders or make do with less metal. Traders obtain some of their metal from the smaller producers, from consumers who sell off surplus metal and from the major producers (how supplies from this last source get on to the free market is best left to the imagination). This trade, however, is likely to be reduced as long as the free market and the producer prices are close to each other.

Cobalt metal prices (free market)   *US dollars per lb*

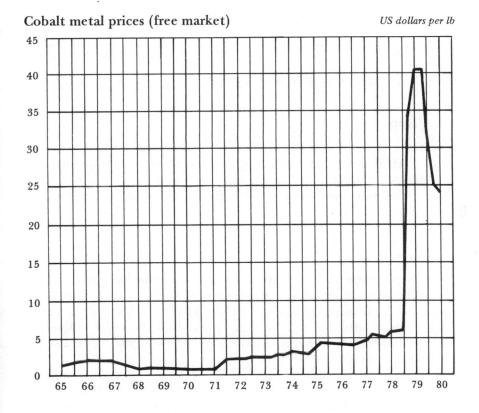

Columbium or Niobium

Columbium ore production, 1977   *ten thousand metric tons*

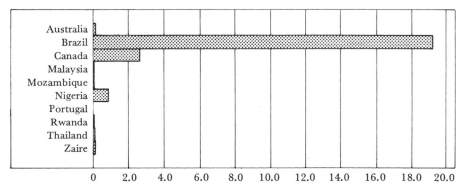

Total world production 26,000 metric tons

Grades available

Pure columbium metal is a rather rare item accounting only for a tiny fraction of total columbium consumption. Its most commonly traded form is ferro-columbium (its alloy with iron) containing from 60-70 per cent columbium. In this form it is sold as irregular lumps packed in drums.

Production method

Columbium is extracted from its naturally occurring ore pyrochlore and from the ore columbite which strangely contains both columbium pentoxide and tantalum pentoxide. If the tantalum content exceeds the columbium content the same basic mineral is known as tantalite. The ore is concentrated by a combination of wet gravity, magnetic and electrostatic processes.

In columbite and tantalite, columbium oxide is separated from the tantalum oxide first by conversion to the fluorides then by a solvent extraction method. The columbium is then reconverted to the oxide by calcining.

Ferro-columbium is produced by the thermic method, that is burning the pentoxide with aluminium powder in the presence of iron powder. Columbium metal can be produced by reducing columbium chloride with magnesium metal.

Major uses

Almost all columbium is used in the form of ferro-columbium and more rarely in the form of the pentoxide in the manufacture of alloy steels. These are in turn used for structural purposes in buildings, bridges, etc, for heavy mining equipment such as rock cutters and for machine components where shock resistance is required. A recent growth area for columbium consumption is in the manufacture of gas and oil pipeline steels. Minor uses for the metal occur in the nuclear energy and electronics industries.

Main market features

Brazil is responsible for producing about 75 per cent of the world's supply of this metal and holds a similar proportion of the world's known reserves. Columbium producers have so far had a very responsible attitude to pricing, with prices rising steadily in line with the growth of consumption and inflation. The effects of the 1974 oil price rise has, however, greatly encouraged the construction of oil pipelines producing an unforeseen demand for columbium. Other metals used for similar purposes including pipeline steels, vanadium and particularly molybdenum, have shown marked price rises which may justify a price rise in columbium. Brazil is in a uniquely powerful position to raise prices if demand justifies such a move. But the competition from vanadium, which can be substituted for columbium in many alloys, needs to be remembered.

Known world reserves

5,100,000 metric tons of columbium (metal content) of which approximately 4 million metric tons are estimated to be in Brazil.

Method of marketing and pricing

Columbium has not been a particularly popular item with metal merchants in the past due mainly to the efficient and flexible pricing policy of main producers who are able to adjust prices and stocks according to demand. They have none of the problems of molybdenum producers, for instance, whose metal is largely a by-product material. Demand in recent times has been stronger, however, and the efforts of the producers to strike a compromise between maintaining a steady market and meeting extra demand may stimulate a small premium market.

Most producers either sell directly to consumers or have local agents to market their product. International merchant activity is only apparent during temporary shortages of material.

Columbium ore prices   *US dollars per lb oxide contained*

Copper

Copper refined production, 1978

million metric tons

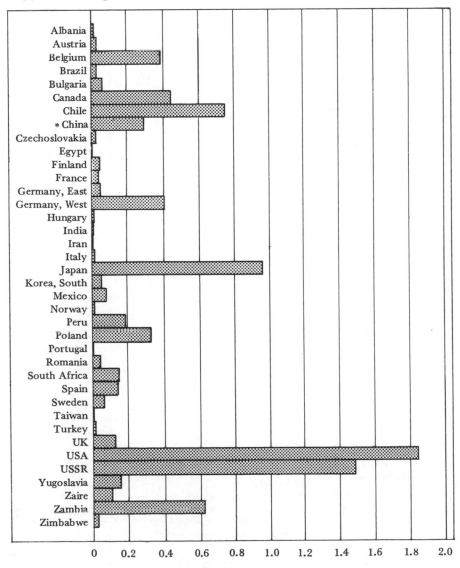

Total world production 9,223,500 metric tons

* & other Asia

Copper refined consumption, 1978

hundred thousand metric tons

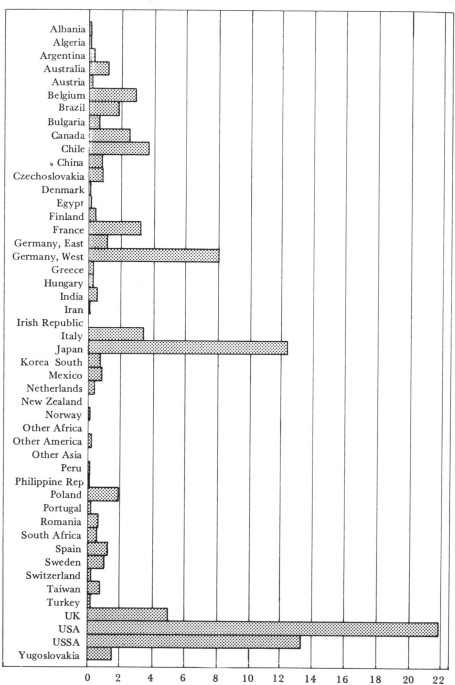

Total world consumption 9,859,900 metric tons   * & other Asia

Grades available

Pure copper is most commonly traded in two forms, cathodes and wirebars.

A cathode is the pure copper slab which results from the electrolytic refining process. Its usual dimension is about 36 ins x 36 ins x ½ in. It has a bubbly surface and a minimum purity of 99.9 per cent copper. This purity includes a small silver content.

Wirebars which are generally cast from cathodes are the elongated ingots used as a starting rod for drawing copper wire. Its standard weight is between 90-125 kg, again with a purity of 99.9 per cent copper plus silver.

Many producers offer grades with certain chemical characteristics such as HCFR (High Conductivity Fire Refined) which is used for applications where high electrical or thermal conductivity is required. Producers also offer fabricated forms such as wires, tubes, sheets etc, but these markets are more the concern of the stockist than the trader or broker.

Production method

There are many types of copper ore but commercially recoverable deposits are either sulphides or, less commonly, oxides. Occasionally, copper is extracted from complex minerals containing other metals such as lead or zinc.

The ores are concentrated by the normal methods of crushing and flotation. Copper salts may be extracted by leaching, that is to say treating the ore with an acid that will preferentially combine with the copper and the resulting copper rich solution can, in turn, be treated to extract the metal. Leaching is particularly useful for refining low grade ores or mine waste. Many copper ores contain other useful non-ferrous metals such as molybdenum, cobalt and selenium and methods to extract these metals in refinable form are incorporated in the copper refining process.

The ores may first be roasted, if the required desulphurization is impossible in the smelting process. The smelter produces an impure form of metal known as blister copper which is cast into large flat ingots. These are used as anodes for the electrolytic refining process which is carried out in the normal way using thin sheets of pure copper as cathodes, onto which the copper is plated.

Major uses

Copper's most familiar uses are as wire for conducting electricity and as its alloy brass for screws and fittings. It is in the electrical industry where most copper is consumed.

Other important uses are as pipes for domestic water supply, in the chemical industry as heat exchangers which include car radiators, refrigerators and industrial cooling systems. The above uses exploit the excellent electrical and thermal conductivity of copper, which are important elements in almost all industries although automobile and electrical cable manufacturing are particularly important consumers.

Another major use is in the manufacture of coinage.

Main market features

The movement of copper prices provides a good indicator of the world's economic state, since it is so widely used throughout industry and elsewhere.

The marketing of copper is greatly influenced by the fact that an increasingly large proportion of supplies, and future reserves, are concentrated in the developing countries, particularly in the African copperbelt running from Zambia to Zaire, and in South America from Chile to Peru. New deposits are likely to be found in the remoter areas of the world, since those in developed areas have been exploited during the long period in which copper has been a major metal utilized by mankind and are gradually becoming exhausted. For the moment the world's two largest producers are the United States and the Soviet Union, but they are also the largest consumers and are, therefore, generally net importers. Canada is another major producer and exporter and Australian production is increasing. Recovery of scrap copper is growing in industrialized countries, providing an additional and major source of supply with a totally different cost structure. A new source of future supply is to come from nodules on the seabed, which have been found to contain an important proportion of copper. But the immediate pattern is for the exploitation of lower grade ores and deposits in remoter areas, as well as increasing supplies of scrap copper.

Known world reserves

275 million metric tons excluding potential re-usable scrap which amounts to some 20 per cent of known reserves.

Method of marketing and pricing

Copper is sold mainly by annual supply contracts, negotiated between consumers and producers. An increasing quantity of copper exports produced in developing countries has come under the control of state organizations selling on a national basis. Developing countries have been seeking to expand their domestic smelting and refining facilities, but copper ore concentrates are sold to smelters in the developed world as well as blister copper. In refined form copper is sold either as wire-bars or as cathodes. Buyers of primary and scrap copper are basically fabricators, who turn it into semi-manufactured forms for sale to industry. Sales often pass through several hands first, including government organizations and merchants.

In the US, the copper industry is to a great extent vertically integrated with the mine producers, who also own smelting and fabricating facilities. This has enabled the US to retain the domestic producer price system, through which the producer fixes the price at which he is prepared to supply copper under long-term contracts. But in 1978 the biggest US producer, Kennecott, decided to abandon its producer price and instead base prices on the New York Copper Exchange (Comex) 'free' market quotations. It was followed by Anaconda, and other US producers have been forced to introduce much more flexible pricing methods. This has introduced a greater instability in copper pricing since New York market quotations tend to be heavily influenced by speculators. Efforts to establish an International Copper Agreement to stabilize prices have, so far, made little progress.

Copper prices (LME cash settlement wirebar)

£ per long ton until 1970 and £ per metric ton from then onwards — annual average

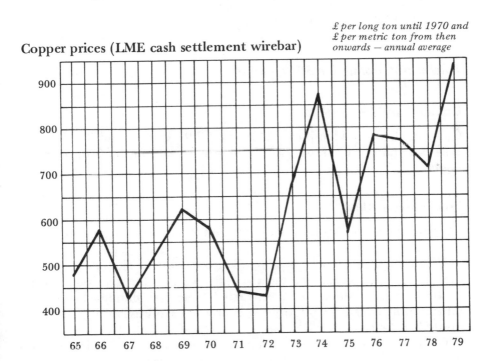

Gallium

£ per long ton until 1070 and £ per metric ton from then onwards — annual average

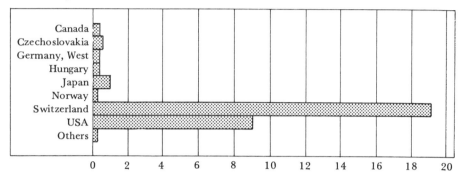

Total world production 30,700 kilos

Grades available

Gallium of a very high purity between 99.9 per cent and 99.9999 per cent is required for most uses. It is usually sold in the form of small ingots.

Production method

All gallium is produced as a by-product of aluminium and zinc production.

It is only extracted from a small proportion of aluminium or zinc ore due to the expense of the process and the low demand in terms of tonnage for gallium. It is extracted from the alumina by precipitation from a caustic solution, then by electrolysis with gallium deposited at the cathode.

Gallium is extracted from zinc concentrates by a simple chemical process and electrolysis, using platinum electrodes.

Major uses

Gallium has two main uses: in electrical semi-conductors and in measuring devices. Its use in semi-conductors represents over 90 per cent of consumption, mainly for diode manufacture.

Main market features

The fact that gallium is a by-product does not mean that the potential for production is limited by the production of the base metal ore from which it is produced, since so little of the main ore is made available for gallium extraction.

Any increase in demand could be met, but time might elapse before plant could be prepared to do this work.

The semi-conductor industry is extremely fickle and regularly changes its requirements for raw material. This means that alternatives for gallium may be found after some technical innovation. On the other hand, it is quite likely that new uses for this metal could arise in some sophisticated application.

No single producer has the power to exercise any great influence over the market, but, as the market is so small and technical, prices remain high to compensate for the stringent level of quality control, and of technical advice that must be offered by any producer.

Gallium metal prices (free market)   *US dollars per kilo*

Method of marketing and pricing

There are very few producers of gallium and all are in industrialized countries where the bulk of consumption occurs. Most producers sell at similar prices direct to consumers. The majority are also large producers of aluminium or zinc and have good marketing arrangements in consuming countries.

Prices vary according to grade, but consumers are as interested in technical reliability as much as price, so there is little scope for merchant activity, except in brief periods of shortage or of selling to state buying corporations.

Germanium

Germanium ore production, 1978

thousand pounds

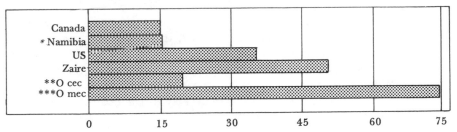

Total world production 195,800 pounds

*S W Africa
** Other central economy countries
*** Other market economy countries

Grades available

Almost all germanium is sold in the form of very high purity ingots or in single crystals. Purity is usually not less than 99.999 per cent minimum, but grades are determined normally by electrical resistivity, the most common being 30 ohm cms or 50 ohm cms.

Production method

All germanium is produced as a by-product of other base metal production, usually zinc or copper.

In zinc ore, germanium oxide is volatilized during the refining process and collected electrostatically.

In copper refining the germanium rich residue is collected magnetically as flue dust and the germanium salt is leached out chemically, then smelted to the metal in a hydrogen atmosphere.

A high degree of purity is required for almost all uses of germanium. This is done by standard zone refining techniques in an electric induction ring.

Major uses

Most germanium is used in the electronics industry for various forms of semi-conductors but a quickly growing use for germanium has been found in the manufacture of various night seeing instruments such as binoculars and gun sights. Other small quantities are used for the production of certain solders.

Main market features

The spectacular rise in the price of germanium in the last year or two has been due to a combination of increased demand, especially for its use in night sights, and a falling production which is partly due to there being less germanium in the mined ore and partly because less zinc is being produced. At current prices, however, it has become more profitable to recover germanium from power station flue dust, where it occurs in greater quantities than it does in zinc ore but in much lower concentrations. This may eventually alleviate the present shortage of material but is unlikely to lower prices greatly as the cost of extraction from both sources is extremely high.

Germanium metal prices (30 ohm) (free market)   *US dollars per kilo*

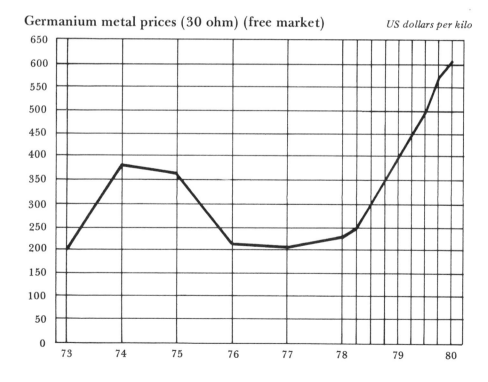

Known world reserves

These are approximately 1,500 tons but this estimate is based on extrapolated production statistics rather than geological data.

Method of marketing and pricing

Because the germanium market is so very small and fickle and marketing so technically orientated, producers need to be well rewarded for their efforts. Prices therefore put germanium into the precious metal class.

Prices vary according to grade and most producers, with perhaps the USSR as the exception, sell at much the same levels. USSR sales are intermittent and, as the price of the metal represents only a small proportion of the value of the component in which it is used, most consumers prefer to rely upon producers who have the best continuity of supply and sound technical reliability.

Merchants have been much more active in recent times and producers can no longer meet demand, but the amount of metal available to the free market, even at large premiums over the producer price, is limited. Even the USSR seems now to be limiting sales.

Indium

Indium metal approximate production, 1978   *hundred thousand troy ounces*

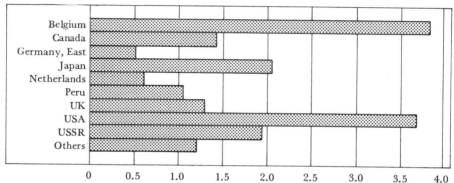

Total world production 1,768,000 troy ounces (approx.)

Grades available

Indium is normally traded in the form of bars or ingots with a minimum purity of 99.99 per cent but some producers still offer a 99.97 per cent grade which is traded at a discount to the normal price.

Production method

All indium is produced commercially as a by-product of zinc and lead production, but only some zinc and lead ores contain indium in recoverable quantities.

    The indium can be recovered by a number of methods, the most common being distillation, but it is also recoverable by leaching and electrolysis.

Major uses

Indium has a wide range of uses: as a thin alloy layer in high performance bearings, mainly for sports cars; in the electronics industry, as a component of transistors and in computer equipment; in low melting point alloys and in solders.

Some of these low melting point alloys are used for glass lens grinding and polishing, and as plugs for fire sprinkler systems.

Indium is also used in catalysts and in the purification system for the manufacture of certain chemical products, particularly man-made fibres. The metal also has many minor uses in research and in laboratory techniques. Small quantities are also used in nuclear reactors.

Main market features

Practically all the uses for indium are either technologically sophisticated or obscure. The electronics industry is notorious for rapidly revolutionizing systems and completely changing its requirements for raw materials. Indium has suffered setbacks in demand as a result of this over the last few years.

Demand from other areas has fluctuated also but, because there are so many uses for this metal, the net effect has been to keep the market surprisingly steady, but in the last few months prices have increased dramatically. Like germanium the increase in price is attributable to increased demand, this time from the electronics industry, and because the zinc ore mined these days contains less indium. The mining of zinc ores which contain useful and expensive by-products is an obvious way for mines to increase their profitability. But such ores are comparatively rare and over the years the content of these metals has diminished, just as the cost of extracting them has increased. Where these by-product metals are used in electronics and for other sophisticated uses, the price of the by-product is bound to increase, especially when the production of the host metal, used mainly in less healthy sectors of the economy, is being curtailed due to lack of demand.

There has been an element of 'speculative' buying interest in indium in recent months, however, which may mean that the indium price may 'level off' as speculators take their profits but high prices must be expected for the foreseeable future.

Method of marketing and pricing

Canada is the largest producer of indium and, together with the producers in the US, maintains a strong but responsible influence on the market. As with many other metals, there are very few large consumers of indium and a multitude of small consumers. The large consumers almost invariably sign their supply contracts with one or other of the large North American producers. This is understandable, as a continuity of supply as well as technical reliability are almost as important as the price.

The price paid by these consumers provides a pricing basis for other producers when selling to smaller consumers but a discounting or premium system exists depending on the state of the market.

There is a small but fairly active free market conducted by the few merchants who specialize in this type of rare metal. Their main source of material is the USSR which conducts a sporadic sales policy. Supplies are also available from Japanese and South American producers who prefer to sell to international merchants rather than to set up their own marketing operation which would be disproportionately expensive owing to the large number of smaller consumers who need to be serviced.

Indium metal prices (free market)   *US dollars per troy ounce*

Lead

Grades available

The most commonly traded grade of refined pig lead is 99.97 per cent minimum. This is the standard minimum grade which can be traded on the London Metal Exchange. There is a large trade in secondary lead (remelted from scrap) which normally has a purity of 99 per cent minimum.

Production method

Lead is found in several minerals, but its most common ore is galena (lead sulphide). Commercially viable lead ores can also be associated with certain zinc bearing minerals. Preparation for smelting varies with the grade of ore. Some high grade material may not need treatment, but low grade ores are concentrated by flotation. The high grade ore concentrate is roasted in air to remove the sulphur, then smelted in a blast furnace or open hearth furnace with coke to reduce the oxide to lead bullion with a purity of about 97 per cent. The bullion is further refined by removing other metal impurities by skimming, after the addition of various reactive chemicals.

Major uses

There is a doubtful future for the use of lead in three important areas. Its most important use in car lead/acid batteries may be short-lived as most authorities believe that lighter, more efficient batteries will replace the lead battery within a decade or so. Its second major use as an additive to petrol is coming under greater scrutiny due to pollution problems. A minor, but still important use in type metal for printing is fast becoming obsolete.

Lead uses for making solders, ammunition and anti-corrosive sheaths for electric cables, however, are still strong markets. Other important minor uses for lead are in anti-radiation shields and as salts in the chemical industry.

Lead refined production, 1978   *hundred thousand metric tons*

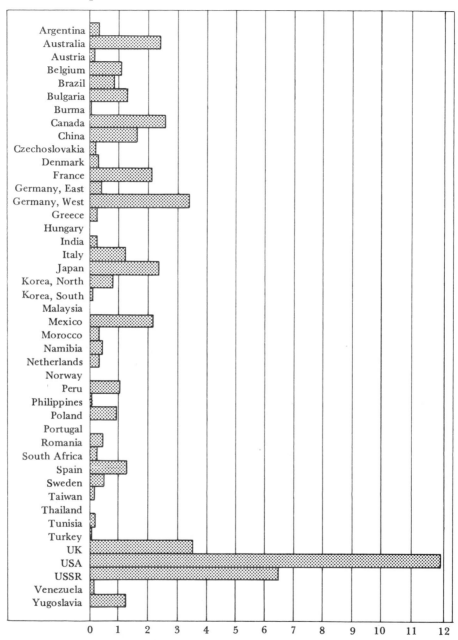

Total world production 5,193,700 metric tons

Lead refined consumption, 1978

hundred thousand metric tons

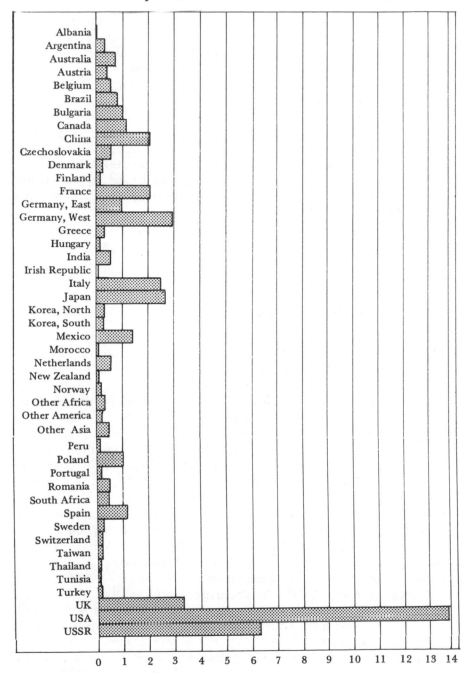

Total world consumption 5,253,100 metric tons

Main market features

Lead is currently supplied mainly from developed countries, notably the United States, but futures reserves are likely to come from developing countries. Lead has been traditionally mined and smelted with its 'sister' metal, zinc, from the same ore bodies. But these metals have different outlets, and an increasing amount of lead is now derived from scrap. The reclamation of lead from batteries and other sources has been highly developed and a good quality grade, competitive with many primary lead outlets, is obtained. An important influence in the lead market is that the growth in demand tends to be steady rather than spectacular. This applies particularly to the batteries market.

In times of economic crisis, batteries are still used by car owners and over the years it has been found that as each use for lead diminishes, such as in pipes and cables, it is replaced by another outlet.

Known world reserves

95 million metric tons

Methods of marketing and pricing

Lead is marketed in a similar manner to copper, which also has a large source of scrap supplies. In North America lead producers operate a fixed producer price system, which applies to sales of refined lead and provides the basis for the cost of ore concentrates bought by refiners. Outside North America the bulk of lead is sold under direct supply contracts between producers and consumers, with prices based on the London Metal Exchange daily quotations.

Since primary lead producers are relatively few in number, and concentrated mainly in developed countries, they have, in the past, exercised considerable influence over the London Metal Exchange market, often keeping up prices by support-buying. In recent years, the threat of anti-cartel action and a large surplus of supplies has diminished this cooperative action by producers. At the same time producers are experiencing greater difficulty in controlling the Metal Exchange price movements in view of the large and increasing proportion of available scrap supplies that are generated if prices are pushed too high. The Metal Exchange itself acts as an important market of last resort for either buyers wanting supplies or sellers disposing of surpluses. In recent years it has been widely used for both these purposes by the communist bloc countries, notably the Soviet Union. Heavy buying by the Soviet Union and other communist countries was primarily responsible for pushing lead prices to an all-time peak in 1979. This emphasized the weakness of a resident market setting prices. The shortage created by the Soviet purchases pushed prices artificially high at a time when there was no scarcity of lead supplies worldwide.

Lead prices (LME cash settlement)

£ per long ton up to 1970 and £ per metric ton from then onwards — annual average

Lithium

Lithium ore production, 1977   *thousand metric tons*

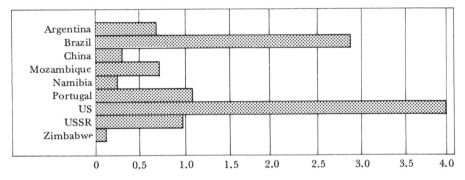

Total world production 10,770 metric tons

Grades available

Pure lithium metal is seldom used or traded. It reacts violently with water so must be kept in strictly dry conditions.

Most applications are for lithium compounds, the most common being lithium carbonate. Other useful compounds are hydroxide, chloride and fluoride.

Production method

Lithium's major ores are petalite, spodumene and lepidolite. It is also found in recoverable quantities in certain brines. The compounds are recovered from the ore by chemical means, either by an acid or alkaline treatment.

These are recovered from brines by a leaching and flotation method after concentration.

Major uses

Lithium is the lightest of all metals, but its uses are limited because of its reaction to water. Small quantities of the metal are used for making light weight alloys in combination with magnesium and aluminium. It is also used as a scavenger and degasifier in the production of steel and as a deoxidizer in melting copper and copper alloys.

The main uses for its compounds are as follows:-

a) *Lithium carbonate* This is used for ceramics, particularly enamels. A comparatively recent but major use is in aluminium smelting where it is added to the molten alumina. Here it has the effect of reducing the temperature at which electrolysis takes place and improves the yield of aluminium production.

b) *Lithium hydroxide* The major use for this compound is in the production of greases.

Lithium compounds are also used in the manufacture of bleaches, disinfectants, synthetic rubber, in welding, brazing and in the glass industries.

Main market features

The only major producers of lithium and lithium compounds are the US and USSR and to a certain extent West Germany. The two major US producers effectively control prices for the Western world but they have to compete with Russian exports outside the US.

There are signs, however, that the USSR is consuming more of its own production lately, thus reducing competition for Western producers.

The US has huge reserves of lithium ore and lithium containing brines, and is not dependent on imports of raw materials.

Reliance on imports of feedstock would limit future production outside lithium ore producing countries.

Known world reserves

6,036,000 tons, of which approximately 4,000,000 are estimated to be in the US.

Method of marketing and pricing

Merchant activity is small and confined to the marketing of USSR material, but the Russians are only intermittent sellers on the world market, so most consumers only buy Russian material to 'top up' supplies.

There is a small amount of competition between Western producers but their prices are usually very similar.

Lithium metal prices

£ per kilo

Magnesium

Magnesium metal production, 1977 *ten thousand metric tons*

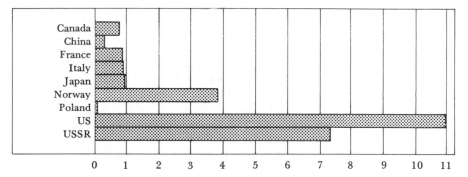

Total world production 259,200 metric tons

Grades available

Magnesium is traded in the form of ingots usually between 5-20kg each with the minimum purity of 99.8 per cent or 99.9 per cent.

Production method

Magnesium is found naturally in the ores magnesite and dolomite, the latter being its principal source in the earlier days of its commercial exploitation. It is now more commonly extracted from brines in salt lakes or seawater. This innovation is likely to represent almost all future production.

Extraction from the ore The ore is first crushed, then thermically reduced with ferro-silicon at high temperatures in retorts. Magnesium comes over as a vapour which is then condensed.

Extraction from brines (magnesium chloride) The chloride is melted in a steel electrolytic cell into which graphite anodes are suspended. The magnesium is released by the passage of a direct electrical current and rises to the surface of the melt where it is tapped into ingot moulds.

Major uses

Magnesium is a metal similar to aluminium, in that it is light and its alloys are strong. It also has many of the same applications.

Magnesium is used in alloy form to make castings, particularly for the aircraft and automobile industries. It is also used in small proportions as an alloy addition in certain aluminium alloys: one of these alloys is used to make the ring-pull type can tops.

Another very important use is in the refining of other metals, notably titanium, where it is used to reduce titanium tetrachloride to the metal.

Ferro-magnesium, usually in the form of ferro-silicon-magnesium, is used in the manufacture of certain cast irons.

Main market features

Magnesium is approximately one third less dense than its rival, aluminium, and its alloys are almost comparable in strength. Theoretically this makes the metal more useful than aluminium for many applications, particularly in transportation.

The technology for the production and working of magnesium has been less advanced than that for aluminium, however, and many potential users have been concerned with the dangers involved in handling the molten or finely divided metal — both can oxidize violently in air. New fluxes and chemical covers can, however, minimize these dangers to a level comparable with those encountered in using aluminium. This should encourage more applications.

World production of magnesium is less than one twentieth of that of aluminium, which automatically increases its unit cost. It is this higher cost which has been the main reason for its comparative lack of development. However, consumption has been growing at a comparable percentage rate with that of aluminium. Magnesium manufacturers have long predicted a future boom in magnesium production once the production grows large enough to reduce unit cost.

Unfortunately, there are very few magnesium producers, partly for the reasons outlined above and partly because production should ideally be sited in an area of low electricity costs. With the advent of production from seawater, however, more sites may be considered suitable.

Prices cannot be expected to rise substantially unless the aluminium price rises disproportionately or unless titanium production is drastically increased.

Known world reserves

Reserves of magnesium are limited only by man's ability to extract it from seawater.

Method of marketing and pricing

With the exception of the USSR, production is confined to industrialized Western countries, which have so far managed to retain a tight grip on the price, particularly as it applies in the country of production.

The rising price of fuel has encouraged motor car manufacturers to reduce the weight of vehicles. As magnesium is a very suitable metal to produce the kind of castings used in motor cars, such as gearbox casings, wheels and even engine blocks, and is an extremely light metal, it is now becoming increasingly popular in the motor car industry. In addition, the high price of titanium is stimulating higher titanium production, which requires magnesium as a fuel. Magnesium consumption is therefore growing. The high price of aluminium will also encourage producers to increase the magnesium price.

Magnesium metal prices (free market)   *US dollars per metric ton*

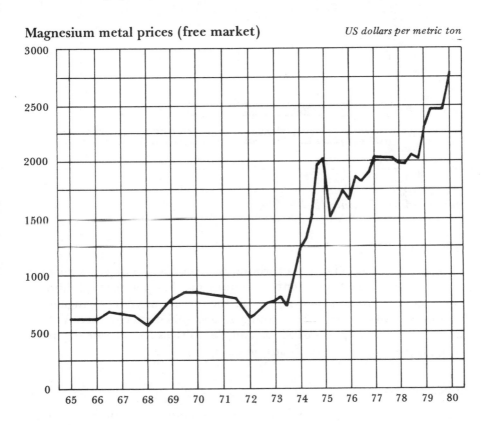

Manganese

Manganese ore production, 1977   *million metric tons*

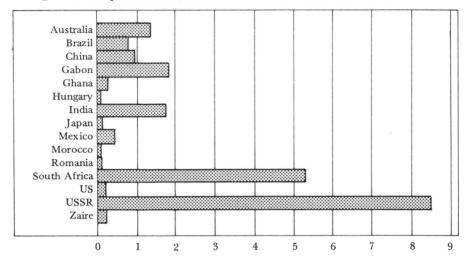

Total world production 22,400,000

Grades available

Pure manganese, usually in the form of an electrolytic lump, is available with a purity of 99.8 per cent minimum or 99.9 per cent minimum. More common forms of manganese on the market are ferro-manganese, with up to 80 per cent Mn content, and silico-manganese, with a content of up to 20 per cent Si, balance Mn. Prices for ferro-manganese vary with the Mn content and carbon contamination.

Production method

Manganese is found naturally in the form of a number of different ores. The ores are concentrated by normal methods which vary according to the type of ore.

    Ferro-manganese is produced by smelting the concentrate in either a blast furnace or an electric arc furnace.

Major uses

About three quarters of all manganese produced is consumed in the form of ferro-manganese used in the manufacture of manganese-containing irons and steels. These are in turn used in a wide variety of applications covering the entire spectrum of industry from construction steels used for bridges, to the steel used for home appliances.

Small proportions of pure manganese are used as an addition to certain aluminium alloys.

Manganese compounds are used in the manufacture of dry cell batteries, in the manufacture of some dyes and bleaches and also to produce several other important chemicals.

Main market features

Although the USSR and South Africa together produce about half the world's manganese (a feature shared with several other metals) there are a number of other important producing countries. Ferro-manganese is produced in an even larger number of countries. It is very difficult for any one producer to control prices, especially as manganese is such a large market.

There is no strict relationship between the price of the ore and ferro-manganese because of the varying cost of production but, because demand for manganese accurately reflects the world's general economic climate, the prices of both have moved historically in unison.

The market in individual consuming countries can be confused because of changing import tariffs.

Known world reserves

Reserves of manganese contained in ore approximately 728 million metric tons. This does not include manganese which may be found on the ocean floor in the form of nodules.

Method of marketing and pricing

Most ferro-manganese is consumed by large companies (iron and steel producers). They usually buy their supplies on long-term contracts directly from producers or producers' agents, or from a merchant, who has in turn bought long-term supplies from the producer. The reason for this style of business is understandable when one considers that ferro-manganese is a very cheap commodity traded in comparatively large tonnages. In order to make prices competitive, material must be shipped directly from producers to the consumers' works. Profit margins per metric ton are generally so small that if material has to be stored awaiting a buyer, or shipped to a port further away than the one originally intended, the extra costs would not be met by profit margins.

The largest producers sell at a producer price but smaller producers and merchants trade on a free market basis at discounts or premiums to the producer price, depending on the state of the market.

Each year the major producers, led by the South Africans, confront their consumers with higher prices, mainly for manganese ore but also for other manganese products. Their success in achieving higher prices depends very much on the ruling market conditions.

There is a small, but active, market in ferro-manganese between merchants and smaller consumers such as cast-iron foundries.

The manganese metal market is not particularly interesting. The metal is consumed mainly by secondary aluminium alloy makers (those utilizing aluminium scrap in their feedstock). There are few large companies of this type, so their intake of manganese is usually only a few metric tons per month. There are merchants who specialize in this type of business, but again they have to compete with producers who sell to the consumers either directly or through agents.

Manganese ore prices   *US dollars per metric ton unit*

Mercury

Mercury metal production, 1977   *ten thousand flasks*

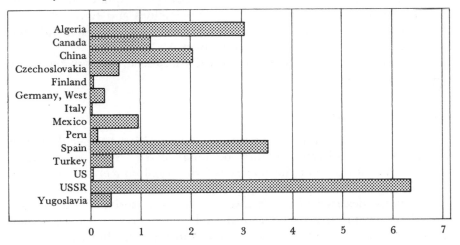

Total world production 206,219 flasks

Grades available

Mercury is sold by the flask, the steel bottle containing 76 lbs of the liquid metal. The standard purity is 99.99 per cent minimum.

Production method

Mercury is produced from its naturally occurring sulphide ore, cinnabar.

The ore is crushed but no attempt is made at further concentration. It is then roasted in retorts and the mercury metal is vapourized and collected. It is a very simple process. In some areas of the world mines produce only two or three flasks per week and are worked by only one or two miners who both excavate and refine the ore.

Major uses

Mercury is an extremely toxic metal. All its uses have come under increasing scrutiny because of its possible effect on the environment.

The best known use for mercury is in thermometers, barometers and pressure gauges, but this accounts for only about 10 per cent of its consumption.

It has three major uses. The first is in the manufacture of chlorine from brine, but other methods can be used to produce chlorine and these are gaining favour for environmental reasons. The second is in batteries, but other types of batteries provide adequate alternatives. The third major use is in agriculture as pesticides and fungicides, but here too environmental considerations have reduced demand and encouraged the use of alternative substances.

Strangely, perhaps, mercury has several important uses in medicine and in dental alloys.

Main market features

Known reserves of mercury are rather small and led to speculation in the 1960's that mercury would become scarce. Such speculation, however, did not predict the recent international concern about pollution. These concerns were reinforced by evidence that mercury has caused many deaths and much disease, the more serious of which are a result of chemical salts being dumped at sea or in rivers and then digested by fish. The mercury accumulates in the fish's body and is thus passed on to humans.

Mercury is the only metal which is in liquid form at normal temperatures and will always find a use for that reason, but where alternative materials can be used they will be used. And these alternative materials probably account for over half the world's current consumption. This notion combined with very low prices has caused most producers, particularly in Spain and Italy, drastically to curtail production and sales. This policy has begun to have some success, especially since the Chinese seem unofficially to have adopted a strategy similar to the main Western producers. They have set a minimum price of $400 per flask on sales and only the very small producers have been willing to sell below this price. This has had the effect of increasing the free market price to just below this level. It would perhaps be too much to expect producers to obtain support from each other to fix the price at much higher than this level for some time to come.

Known world reserves

Commercially viable ore contains approximately 3,200,000 flasks.

Method of marketing and pricing

There are no effective international producer prices for mercury. All producers have to sell at a free market price, but many large orders for the metal are purchased on a tender basis, where merchants and producers alike submit offers and the cheapest offer wins the contract. In the depressed circumstances of the mercury market consumers have had the upper hand.

In the 1960s there was a very active and important market in mercury which attracted many large trading houses. With the combination of low prices, low turnover and the absence of price movements, there are now few merchants specializing in this trade.

Scrap recovery

There is a fair trade in scrap mercury, usually carried out on a local basis. This material can be cleaned by filtration or by distillation.

Mercury prices (free market)   *US dollars per flask of 76 lbs net*

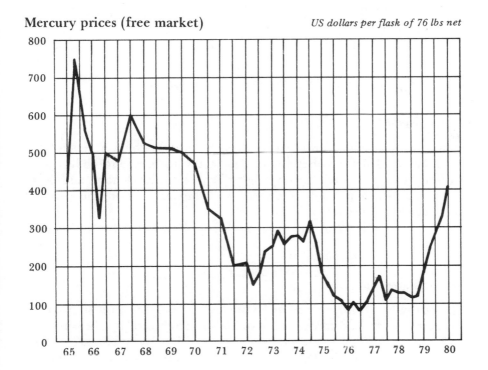

Molybdenum

Molybdenum ore production, 1977   *ten thousand metric tons MoS$_2$ content*

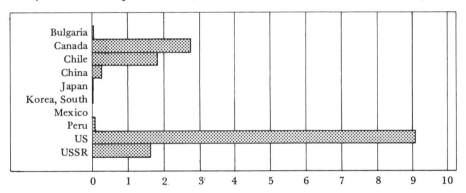

Total world production 157,000 metric tons MoS$_2$ content

Grades available

There is only a small world consumption of molybdenum in its metallic form. The bulk of the metal is traded in the form of molybdic oxide (MoO3) or ferro-molybdenum, the alloy of molybdenum and iron, containing between 60-80 per cent molybdenum or in the form of its concentrated ore (sulphide).

The few producers of the pure metal supply it in the form of ingots, sheet and wire.

Production method

The naturally occurring ore, molybdenite, a molybdenum sulphide, is concentrated by flotation. The oxide is produced by heating the sulphide in air. The oxide can then be purified by sublimation. The material is produced by the reduction of the pure oxide in the presence of hydrogen at high temperatures. Between one quarter and one third of the world's production of molybdenum is produced as a by-product of copper production when the copper ore contains a high proportion of molybdenum.

Major uses

The pure metal has a small but increasing application in highly technical industries such as nuclear energy, aerospace and electronics.

Its main application by far is as an alloy addition to steel. Its effect on steel in additions of about 1 per cent is much like that of chromium and nickel: it increases strength and toughness especially at high temperatures. Such steels find applications in the production of mining equipment and machine components and have a growing use in oil pipelines.

Major market features

The US is much the largest producer of molybdenum and it is produced there by only a few companies. These companies are therefore in a powerful position to control the market price. They publish a producer price for their major products which is adhered to but they ration material to their customers in times of shortage. Supply is somewhat affected by fluctuations in copper production but, strangely, not much affected by the steel market variations due to the special applications of molybdenum steels, the uses of which may be somewhat out of phase with general economic conditions. The development of the oil industry is particuarly relevant to demand due to its application in pipelines and refineries.

Demand for molybdenum from every sector has increased tremendously in the last year or two. It has completely outstripped supply and caused a major shortage and an attendant remarkable price rise. High prices have, however, stimulated increased production ventures, which should bring supply and demand into balance by about 1983. Speculation in molybdenum exacerbated the shortage in 1979 and the sales of these stocks has helped to bring the price down to more reasonable levels. One cannot expect much of a further fall in price, however, as production costs increase and demand remains high.

Known world reserves

Approximately 4,900,000 metric tons of which 3 million metric tons are estimated to be in the United States.

Method of marketing and pricing

Molybdenum prices in the form of sulphide, oxide and ferro-molybdenum are quoted as a price per pound or per kilogram of molybdenum content.

Free market trade is somewhat intermittent, drying to a trickle in times of supply/demand balance but flaring up into hectic trading in times of shortage. This trade is conducted by comparatively few international trading houses which usually specialize in all the refractory metals, that is, vanadium, columbium, titanium and tungsten.

Molybdenum ore prices (producer price)   *US dollars per lb Mo contained*

Nickel

Nickel metal production, 1978   *ten thousand metric tons*

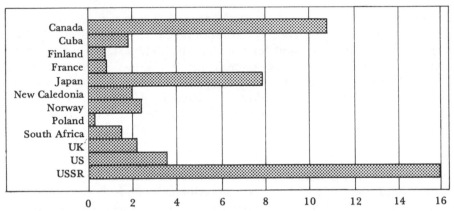

Total world production 611,600 metric tons

Grades available

Nickel comes in many shapes, sizes and purities to suit the various uses to which it is put.

Cathodes These are produced by electrolytic means and are either full size (un-cut) up to 750mm x 750mm or cut into smaller squares for convenience. These squares range from 1in x 1in up to 10ins x 10ins. The full size cathodes are cut into squares using a power shear, so they are only roughly square. The smaller squares are always more expensive than the larger ones as more cuts have to be made. As a very rough guide, 10ins squares are about two US cents per pound more than un-cut cathodes, but 1in x 1in squares may be 10 US cents per pound or more above the price of 10in x 10in squares. The thickness of cathodes varies with the producer, but generally is about 1cm. The smaller squares may be used for electroplating.

Minimum purity is usually 99.8 per cent with a maximum cobalt content of 0.1 per cent.

Briquettes These are small, regular shaped lumps of compressed nickel matte (spongy granules of pure nickel). They can be a variety of shapes — tablet, round or square, but generally no bigger than 2½ins in the largest dimension.

Granules These are solid pure nickel in granular form.

Pellets and Shot These are made by the largest producers.

Ferro-nickel An alloy of nickel and iron usually containing about 30 per cent nickel.

Nickel oxide This is known sometimes as sinter, usually in briquetted form.

These are the main types of nickel traded. There are premiums and discounts depending on the type of material: cathodes and pure pellets are the most expensive and ferro-nickel the cheapest. All prices move up and down in unison. To complicate the situation further, some origins of metal may be more expensive than others. The best guide to price movements is the market for Russian 10in x 10in cathodes which are probably the most commonly traded on the free market.

Production method

Almost all nickel is mined as nickel ore rather than as a by-product of other metal ores. The ore is either an oxide or a sulphide of nickel. The sulphide ores are crushed and concentrated by flotation but with laterite (oxide ore) no concentration method has been found effective.

Where nickel is found in conjunction with copper, the nickel may be separated by a combination of magnetic and flotation techniques and by recrystallization. Sulphides are converted to oxides by roasting in air and the oxides reduced to the metal in a reverberatory furnace. Where nickel ore contains cobalt or other secondary metals separation is by chemical means.

Major uses

Nickel has a vast number of uses throughout industry. The most commonly known use must be in coins when alloyed with copper, and in stainless steel when alloyed with iron and chromium. It is used in metallic and salt form with and without other metals and salts, as a catalyst in a large range of inorganic chemical reactions. Many types of steel alloys contain nickel especially when resistance to corrosion is required. It is used for plating, especially in the automobile industry and for cutlery. Some types of batteries use nickel. It forms part of many high strength alloys used in the aircraft industry. Stainless steel can be made with several other metals but nickel is by far the most competitive in cost.

Main market features

Historically nickel has been produced by a limited number of powerful groups led by International Nickel of Canada, who at one stage had over 80 per cent of the western world market. However, the last 10 years have seen dramatic changes in the structure of the industry with the entry of many newcomers and International Nickel's share has been cut down to below 35 per cent. The turnround started in 1969 when a long strike at the Canadian mines of Inco, and Falconbridge, resulted in a severe shortage of supplies. This forced consumers to look for alternative sources, or substitutes for nickel, and attracted new producers into what then became a highly competitive market. Canadian sulphide deposits remain the main source of nickel at present, but the bulk of future reserves are in laterite deposits.

Method of marketing and pricing

The London Metal Exchange commenced nickel trading in 1979. This move coincided with another short strike in Canada's nickel mines. The combination of these events, stimulated by speculative interest through the LME, had the effect of increasing the price dramatically, even though there was no physical shortage of the metal throughout this period.

Nickel metal prices (free market) *US dollars per lb*

The LME is now by far the biggest influence on the nickel price, although most of the larger consumers still buy their requirements directly from the producers.

Demand for nickel has been falling in recent months, due to the general decline in industrial activity, and the increasing competition from the smaller producers is expected to have the effect of reducing prices.

Known world reserves

Approximately 90 million metric tons.

Rhenium

Rhenium metal production, 1978   *thousand kilos*

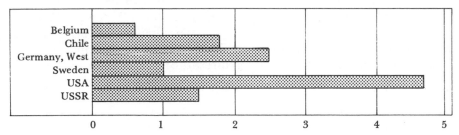

Total world production 12,100 kilos

Grades available

The major rhenium producers offer a variety of metallic forms and compounds but most international trade is conducted in metallic powder with a purity of 99.99 per cent minimum and in ammonium perrhenate $NH_4 ReO_4$ containing 69 per cent rhenium.

Production method

Rhenium was isolated comparatively recently, in 1925, and has only been used commercially since the early 1950s. It is produced commercially only as a by-product of molybdenum production, where it occurs in copper-molybdenum porphyry ore bodies. It is recovered from the flue ducts and gases produced during the roasting of the molybdenum concentrates.

Major uses

The most important uses for rhenium are as catalysts used to reform petroleum, in the production of high octane petrol and in the production of benzene, toluene, xylenes and other organic compounds.

Its other important uses are in lamp filaments, thermocouples and electrical contacts.

Main market features

Although rhenium is not a platinum group metal, it has very similar physical and chemical properties to those of platinum. Its uses are similar but, unlike platinum, which is found in recoverable quantities only in very few areas, rhenium is found in most copper-molybdenum ores.

Some 30 tons of rhenium contained in ore are mined every year but only about one third of this production is extracted, either because the molybdenum producer has no extraction plant or because low rhenium prices in the past have made extraction unprofitable. However, during 1979 prices trebled. This was because rhenium can be used as a substitute for platinum. In practice rhenium is used in a platinum/rhenium compound which not only reduces the amount of platinum used in the catalyst but also improves the efficiency of the catalytic effect. Platinum prices rose dramatically as a result of a combination of investment speculation, increased consumption and restricted sales from the USSR.

Although high prices will encourage increased production, there is no reason to suspect that prices will fall. Demand is high, especially for its use as a catalyst, and American consumers are impressed with the fact that they do not have to rely on South Africa or the

Rhenium metal prices   *US dollars per kilo*

USSR for rhenium supplies, as they would for supplies of platinum group metals. The USA in fact is the largest producer of rhenium.

Even if it were possible to extract all the rhenium from mined molybdenum ore, production would still not satisfy the demand for catalyst metals in the petrochemical industry.

Assuming that the shortage of platinum will continue, rhenium prices will remain high.

Known world reserves

Approximately 3,500 tons, of which 1,300 tons are in the USA and 1,200 tons in Chile.

Method of marketing and pricing

Until the increased demand for rhenium occurred in 1979 there was almost no merchant activity in the rhenium market. The shortage of metals has encouraged a fairly active market, however, conducted by specialist metal merchants who obtain most of their supplies from the USSR and the smaller molybdenum refineries. Small quantities are recovered from the treatment of scrap rhenium.

It is rather unlikely that the major producers will be in a position to meet consumer demand but the recent increase in price for both rhenium and molybdenum will stimulate increased production, which will go some way towards alleviating the current shortage.

Selenium

Selenium metal production, 1977   *hundred thousand kilos*

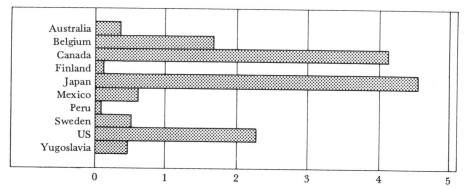

Total world production 1,500,000 kilos

Grades available

Selenium is usually made available in the form of powder or granules and most commonly traded as a fine powder (minus 200 mesh) with a purity of either 99.5 per cent or 99.8 per cent minimum.

Production method

Almost all selenium is produced as a by-product of copper production. Selenium-rich slimes are recovered from the anode during the electrolytic refining of copper. To produce the elemental selenium these slimes are treated with sulphuric acid and the metal is then precipitated by a simple chemical operation.

Major uses

The five major uses of selenium are rather sophisticated and it should be noted that, in each, the cost of the metal is small compared with the system or process in which it is used. These uses divide the consumption roughly equally but change slightly according to technical innovation.

It is used in the manufacture of certain types of glass as a decolourizer. In the electronics industry it is used in the manufacture of transformers, semi-conductors and photo-electric cells. Selenium has a unique use in photocopying machines, transferring a photographic image by means of static electricity. The metal is used in combination with cadmium to make an orange/red pigment used extensively in plastics and ceramics. The remaining major use is as an addition to steels, mainly stainless steel, to improve forging characteristics. There are several very minor uses for selenium in the chemical, pharmaceutical, rubber and explosives industries.

Main market features

Selenium has one of the world's most volatile markets. It has all the classic ingredients of volatility: it has a small production, which makes it suitable for market manipulation; the demand for selenium is only fractionally reduced by high prices as explained above; and it is a by-product which sets an upper limit on production.

In times of shortage its value can change by hundreds of per cent only to fall by similar values when consumption declines. Fortunately its production is rather widespread compared with many materials, and no single producer is in a position completely to control prices.

Demand has remained fairly static for some time now and, in spite of the high level of speculation in other similar metals, such as cadmium and bismuth, during 1979 and 1980, selenium did not attract the attention of non-trade buyers.

Known world reserves

Approximately 80,000 tons.

Method of marketing and pricing

North American producers publish a producer price for the metal which they adhere to fairly strictly. Other producers may base supply contracts on this producer price but are increasingly marketing on the basis of free market quotations. This gives them the obvious advantage of making very large profits from the metal in times of shortage and prevents them from having to keep stocks of material in times of over-supply, as the North Americans are sometimes obliged to do, to protect their price.

The free market is fed particularly by material refined in Japan. International trading is conducted by merchants mainly in London, Dusseldorf and Brussels.

Selenium metal prices (free market)   *US dollars per pound*

Silicon

Silicon metal production, 1978 — *ten thousand metric tons*

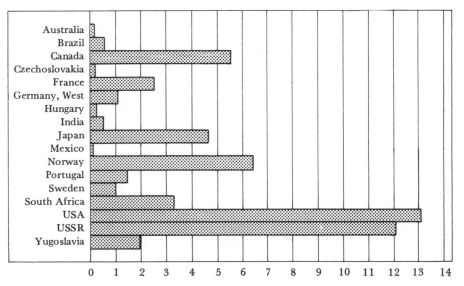

Total world production 549,000 metric tons

Grades available

Most silicon is marketed in the form of irregular lumps usually between 10-100mm in size. The most commonly accepted purity is 98.5 per cent minimum with maximum iron and calcium contents of 0.5 per cent and 0.3 per cent respectively. When silicon is used in the chemical industry, higher purities are often required.

Most silicon is consumed in the form of ferro-silicon, an alloy of silicon and iron. The most popular grade contains 75 per cent silicon.

Production method

High grade quartzite sands and pebbles are the raw material for both silicon metal and ferro-silicon. These are mixed with coke in the production of silicon and with both coke and scrap iron in the production of ferro-silicon, and then smelted in a powerful electrical arc furnace. The raw materials for both products are extremely cheap. The cost of production is mainly the cost of electrical energy. Production plants are usually sited in areas with low cost electricity and often linked to large hydro-electric plants.

Major uses

Approximately 90 per cent of all silicon is produced in the form of ferro-silicon which is consumed in the iron and steel industry as an alloying agent. Consumption is divided roughly equally between steel and cast iron manufacturing.

About 75 per cent of all silicon metal produced is consumed in the aluminium industry where it is used to make aluminium alloys of a type that is used in castings.

Silicon metal (silicon is not strictly a metal in chemical terms and is sometimes referred to as a metaloid) is also used as a de-oxidizer in steel production and in the manufacture of silicones used as waxes, lubricants and polishes.

Main market features

Although we are concerned here with the marketing of pure metals rather than alloys, we must in this case take the ferro-silicon market into account because many plants producing ferro-silicon can be adapted to producing silicon metal and vice versa.

Aluminium and iron ore have such wide applications that the markets of these metals reflect the general state of world economic conditions. As nearly all silicon is used in these two industries it follows that the silicon market is governed in the same way. A higher growth rate for aluminium over steel is predicted which will encourage silicon rather than ferro-silicon production, but silicon production requires more energy to produce than ferro-silicon plus a higher grade of raw material.

Many countries with spare electric power have been attracted to silicon production because the raw material is cheap and relatively common. Electricity is often a difficult commodity to export and production plants are fairly unsophisticated. These countries assume that silicon is like a solid storable exportable form of electrical power.

Prices, however, have not increased even remotely in line with energy prices, mainly because of the severe competition between producers, none of whom is making enough profit to contemplate future increased production. Silicon is an extremely useful metal and demand continues to grow in the aluminium and silicone sector. These factors, combined with the continuing escalation of fuel prices, must mean higher prices, especially for metallic silicon in the future, and may mean a really rapid increase in price in a year or two when demand will almost certainly outstrip the rather low expansion rate of supply.

Known world reserves

Silicon is one of the world's most common elements. Reserves are so enormous that there is no point in estimating them.

Method of marketing and pricing

Ferro-silicon, ferro-manganese and ferro-chrome are known as bulk ferro-alloys and they are traded quite differently from silicon metal. Ferro-silicon is marketed to steel mills in very large tonnages often more than 1,000 tons at a time, either directly by the producers or very often through their agents. There are comparatively few steel mills, so trade is highly competitive, except in times of shortage. There are, however, very many cast iron foundries which buy in quite small quantities from producers' agents and merchants who specialize in the trading and distribution of bulk ferro-alloys. Most of these merchants are small, nationally based companies, but there are

Silicon metal prices (free market) *US dollars per metric ton*

several very large international merchants trading in larger tonnages who often have agency agreements with the producers.

There are comparatively loose forms of producer price control but most trade is subject to supply and demand.

Silicon metal is also distributed directly by producers or their agents at a ruling producer price, but there is a large and active free market in the metal. The Scandinavian producers are the most successful at maintaining a producer price. Merchants in silicon metal are usually different from those trading in ferro-silicon. The material they deal in comes mainly from Yugoslavia and Spain, and from that which is offered for export by producers outside the country of production.

Sodium

Sodium metal production, 1978 *ten thousand metric tons*

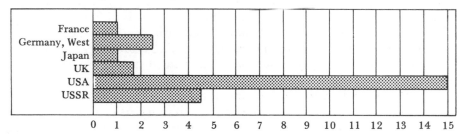

Total world production 247,000 metric tons

Grades available

Sodium is an extremely soft metal which reacts violently with water. It is usually sold in the form of sticks or blocks which have to be protected from water in the atmosphere by submerging in oil or by placing in airtight drums.

Production method

Sodium is produced electrolytically from molten sodium chloride (common salt).

Major uses

About 80 per cent of production is used to make the anti-knocking agents tetraethyl and tetramethyl lead used in petrol. Its other major uses are in the manufacture of titanium metal (magnesium metal can also be used for this purpose) and as a coolant in nuclear reactors.

Main market features

There is very little merchant activity in sodium. This is mainly because there are few producers in the world, and the main producers also manufacture the anti-knocking compounds, which are the biggest outlet for this metal. The USSR does export material from time to time but only when in surplus to its own requirements.

Known world reserves

Reserves of raw material are only as limited as the salt in the ocean.

Method of marketing and pricing

The market price of sodium is based only on its cost price. The raw material costs next to nothing and the main costs of production are electricity and handling, which have been rising rapidly. Competition is not particularly fierce for the reasons outlined above and because of the danger of moving the material over long distances, or storing for long periods of time. All major consumers buy direct from producers who sell at a similar price in the same market.

As there is practically no free market activity in sodium metal the price is controlled by the major producers who currently sell at about 50¢ per lb in the United States and £750 per metric ton in Europe.

These prices have risen by approximately 10 to 15 per cent per annum over the last three years.

Tantalum

Tantalum ore estimated production, 1976 *hundred metric tons (Ta$_2$O$_5$ contained)*

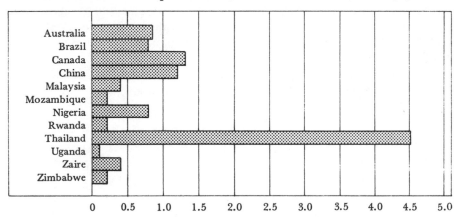

Total world production (1979) 1230 metric tons

Grades available

Most tantalum is traded in the form of its ore, tantalite, which is sold in two main grades: that containing a minimum of 60 per cent Ta$_2$O$_5$; and that containing approximately 30 per cent Ta$_2$O$_5$.

There is very little trade in metallic tantalum, but the producers' main products are powder, sheet and bar of 99.9 per cent minimum purity.

Production methods

Tantalum oxide is extracted from its natural occurring ores, tantalite and columbite (the two often occur together). The oxide is first concentrated by magnetic separation and the metal is then produced by electrolytic means.

Major uses

Like tungsten and columbium, tantalum is one of the refractory metals. It has a high melting point and is very resistant to corrosion. In the past it was added to steel to make alloys similar to those made with columbium. The discovery of adequate deposits of columbium ore which is less dense than tantalum has almost eliminated the use of tantalum as a steel additive.

Tantalum's corrosion resistance has found many applications in the chemical industry where it is used to make pipes, crucibles, retorts, etc.

The electronics industry is tantalum's biggest consumer. Here its largest use is in the manufacture of capacitors, where it is used in the form of powder produced from tantalum oxide by first converting the oxide to the fluoride. It is also used to produce components such as contact points and electrodes.

Small quantities of tantalum carbide are used in cutting tools and even smaller quantities of the metal are used in surgery to make clips and struts to repair veins and bones.

Tantalum ore prices   *US dollars per lb Ta_2O_5 contained*

Main market features

Demand for tantalum for its use in capacitors has increased considerably in the past year or two and, as there has been very little increase in production, the price of the ore has trebled in the past 12 months. High prices have started to stimulate increased production, however. The uses of tantalum in other areas is likely to be reduced as the price rises, since alternative metals can be used as a substitute.

The electronics industry is one of the few sectors of world industry to remain unaffected by the general decline in the economy and demand for tantalum will remain high. The main producers exercise a great deal of control over supplies and one cannot expect prices to fall back by very much in the foreseeable future.

Method of marketing and pricing

Tantalum ore has an important application for making refractories (used for furnace linings, etc) outside its use as a raw material for making tantalum.

All tantalum metal producers maintain a close relationship with consumers and are often required to make the semi-fabricated parts that consumers require. These products may have a strict degree of technical tolerance which is reflected in the price.

Most merchant activity is restricted to the trading of tantalum ore but some merchants trade in scrap tantalum, which is usually recycled back to the producers.

Tellurium

Tellurium metal production, 1977   *ten thousand kilos*

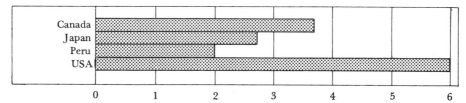

Total world production 145,000 kilos

Grades available

Tellurium is usually marketed in the form of small ingots or slabs, or in the form of fine powder. The purity of commercial grade material is normally between 99.7 per cent and 99.9 per cent minimum.

Production method

Tellurium is only produced as a by-product of other metals, particularly copper, but it may be present in commercially recoverable quantities in certain zinc and lead ores. Tellurium containing slimes are recovered from the anode during the electrolytic refining of copper. These slimes are leached with caustic soda. Tellurium oxide is then precipitated from the solution by acidification and the oxide is roasted to the metal and refined.

Major uses

Tellurium is used as an alloy addition, in very small proportions to certain steels and copper alloys. In both cases the tellurium content improves the machinability of the alloy. It may be added to iron and steel in the form of ferro-tellurium containing about 50 per cent tellurium, the balance is iron.

Its addition to steels reduces porosity and acts as a grain refiner.

The compounds have various uses in the chemical industry in ceramics, rubber vulcanization and in detonators and pesticides. However, these chemical uses only amount to about 10 per cent of the tellurium market.

An alloy of bismuth and tellurium displays unique electro-thermic characteristics, but no major industrial application has yet been found for this property.

Main market features

Tellurium's uses are of no particular importance and all have known substitutes, but tellurium is preferred to other products at current commecial differentials.

Only about half of the potential supply of tellurium in copper ore is utilized at present, due to the cost of its extraction. Any future increase in demand could be met quite easily by improving extraction techniques.

Prices are likely to keep in line with the increased cost of production, but any future growth in demand may lead to a temporary price rise while production is being increased.

Tellurium metal prices   *US dollars per pound*

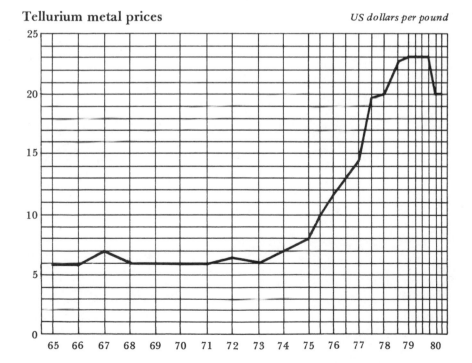

Known world reserves

Approximately 50,000 tons of tellurium metal.

Method of marketing and pricing

The tellurium market is very small and its supply/demand characteristics have not attracted much merchant activity. The major producers
handle most of the marketing directly or through agents. Prices are
fixed by producers, but some business is done on a free market basis,
especially that between producers and state-owned buying corporations,
often with a merchant as intermediary.

Tin

Tin refined production, 1978

thousand metric tons

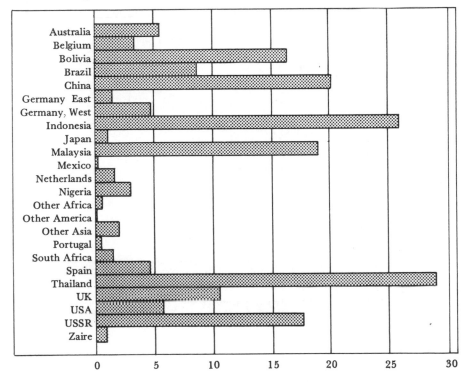

Total world production 236,900 metric tons

Grades available

Tin is sold on the international market in ingot form (up to 50kg each) with a purity of 99.75 per cent or at a premium price for high grade material with a purity of 99.85 per cent minimum.

Tin refined consumption, 1978

ten thousand metric tons

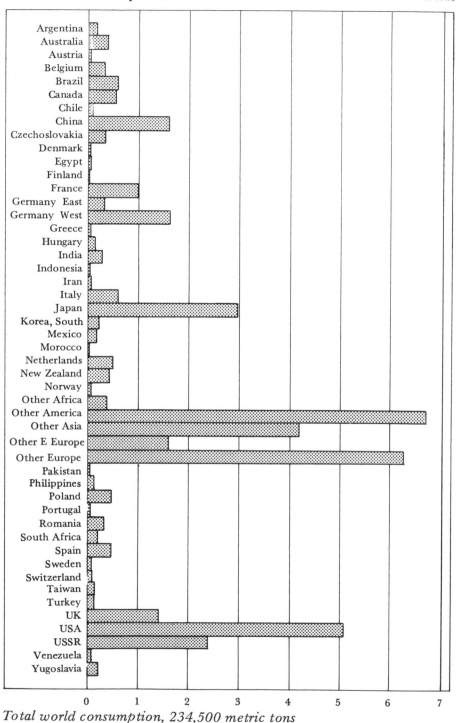

Total world consumption, 234,500 metric tons

Production method

Tin's main ore, cassiterite (tin oxide) is mainly found in alluvial deposits in river beds and deltas and recovered by dredging methods. It is also recovered by the gravel pump mining method, and by traditional mining in such areas as Bolivia.

The ore, either from dry or wet deposits, is usually concentrated by magnetic or electrostatic means and the concentrate is smelted with coke in a reverberatory furnace to reduce it to metal.

Major uses

The major user of tin is still the canning industry. Tin cans, used for packaging food and drink, are made of steel sheet, plated with a thin layer of tin. This material is known as tinplate which is rolled from a large slab of steel clad with tin. Tin is an important constituent of most solders and other alloys such as babbit metal and bronze.

Main market features

Tin is found in relatively few countries. Malaysia is by far the biggest producer, followed by Bolivia, Indonesia, Thailand, China, the Soviet Union, Australia, Brazil, Nigeria, Zaire and the United Kingdom. It is one of the few metals found only in limited quantities on the North American continent. But the United States holds a strategic stockpile, equal to about one year's total world consumption. No major new deposits of tin have been discovered for many years, but the development of offshore mining has to an extent offset the gradual exhaustion of land deposits. Improved mining techniques, and higher price levels, have also made practical the exploitation of deposits with a far lower tin content and encouraged the reworking of 'tailings' from old mines. Over half the world's refined tin metal is smelted in Malaysia, at Penang, where the smelters produce the top quality Straits tin. Indonesia and Thailand have their own domestic smelters. Bolivia is building up its smelting facilities, but still exports a large proportion of its ore concentrates to smelters in Europe, notably the United Kingdom. China is expected to become a net importer of tin in the 1980s, as a result of expansion in its domestic tin plate industry. The switch, by China, from exporting to importing could have a serious impact on the world tin supply/demand balance in the years ahead.

There is some reclamation of tin previously used, but since the main outlet is as a thin coating on steel to produce tinplate, scrap recovery is limited. Historically, demand for tin has had a very low annual growth rate which usually fluctuates in accordance with the state of the steel industry. There has been strong competition from so-called 'tin

free' steel — that is tinplate with another metal such as chrome replacing tin — and from aluminium in the beverage cans market.

Known world reserves

6.5 million metric tons

Method of marketing and pricing

Tin is marketed in a variety of ways: by supply contracts between
governments or individual companies with consumers; through
merchants; or through the Penang smelters or London Metal Exchange.
Another supply source is the United States stockpile, which sells by
competitive bids.

The two main pricing centres are the Penang market in Malaysia
which is the main physical market and the London Metal Exchange.
The smelters daily offer for sale a quantity of tin equal to the
intake of ore concentrates received from miners. Buyers put in their
bids, and under a complicated formula the smelters calculate an average
price for that day of the tin available for sale. They take the top price
bids down to the point where all the tin available has been bidden for,
and the bid, at that cut-off point, becomes the average price.

The London Metal Exchange tin market trades in tin for delivery
up to three months ahead, although individual dealers will provide
quotations for even further forward. It has the only futures 'hedging'
mechanism which gives protection against price fluctuations. (The
Malaysian Government is at present planning a tin futures market.)
The London Metal Exchange warehouses attract supplies from all
over the world, including Malaysia, so there is a physical trade business
as well as a 'paper' futures market.

Prices for supply contracts are often based on a mixture of quotations
from the Penang and London Metal Exchange, and there is a great
deal of arbitrage between the two markets if one or other moves out
of line.

The tin market has a long history of price volatility but in the past
20 years it has been controlled to a large extent by the International
Tin Agreement, between producers and consumers. The agreement
defines 'floor' and 'ceiling' price levels and attempts to keep prices
between these limits by the use of a buffer stock mechanism, backed
on occasions by export quotas. The Agreement has been largely ineffective since January 1978 when the buffer stock supply was exhausted and market prices rose above the 'ceiling' level. Despite subsequent increases in the Tin Agreement price ranges, market values
remained above the 'ceiling' making the Agreement virtually inopera-
tive.

The Fifth Tin Agreement expires in June 1981 and considerable difficulty is anticipated in negotiating a new Agreement. Producers want to strengthen the existing Agreement by ensuring that it provides them with more control. The US, however, wants a new Agreement with a larger buffer stock but no export quotas. The US is by far the biggest consumer of tin and is concerned to secure adequate supplies since it has virtually no domestic production. An important influence on the market has been the US strategic stockpile, built up after the Korean War, which still holds the equivalent of about a year's world consumption. Stockpile releases have been used in the past to fill the shortfall between new production and demand. The US resumed tin stockpile sales in July 1980 following Congress authority for 30,000 tons to be released. After consultations with the International Tin Council, the US decided to spread the stockpile sales over three years with an annual offering of 10,000 tons.

Tin prices (LME standard tin-cash settlement)

£ per long ton up to 1970 and £ per metric ton from then onwards — annual average

Titanium

Titanium sponge estimated production, 1980   *thousand metric tons*

Total world production 92,900 metric tons

Grades available

Titanium's uses are of a highly technical nature. Many producers are therefore obliged to make titanium in several sizes and forms, that is slabs, sheet, bars, wire and other semi-fabricated types, but pure titanium is traded mainly in the form of sponge (irregular granules) or briquettes (compressed blocks of sponge). This material is usually of 99.6 per cent minimum purity.

Production method

The metal is produced by first converting the ore, rutile or ilmenite into titanium dioxide by means of a simple chemical treatment. The dioxide is then converted to the tetrachloride and heated with magnesium or sodium which reduces it to the metal.

Major uses

There are many independent industrial uses for both the ore and the oxide. Titanium metal's physical properties, its lightness, strength and resistance to corrosion have resulted in many new uses for the metal in modern times. It has been found particularly useful in the aerospace industry, where it is used for such items as turbine blades, engine shafts and in the framework and skins of spacecraft and high performance aircraft. Its resistance to corrosion makes the metal suitable for applications such as pipes, pumps and containers in the chemical industry and in electro-plating. The metal has found an increasing use as an alloy addition in certain steels, some of which are used in automobile silencers (mufflers). It is added to steel either as pure titanium or in the form of ferro-titanium, a master alloy which is made by melting scrap titanium and iron, or by direct reduction of the ore with iron.

Main market features

The boom in both the civil and military aircraft industry has created an unprecedented demand for titanium metal which has caused prices to rise to unprecedented levels. Production increases have not yet been able to meet this demand but large increases in production capacity are planned by most of the major producers. The high price has also stimulated greater efforts to recycle scrap titanium. Titanium production is confined to a very few manufacturers in industrialized countries. These countries are also the major consumers of this metal.

Known world reserves

Titanium metal in ore is approximately 4,350,000 metric tons. However, titanium can be extracted from other minerals less competitively.

Titanium (sponge) metal prices (free market)   *US dollars per kilo*

Method of marketing and pricing

The producers of titanium control its price in the country of production. Their price is limited only by the price of imported titanium products from other countries. There is, however, a small free market trade in metal originating from the USSR, usually in the form of sponge or briquettes. Small quantities are also available from Japan and very recently from China in the form of sponge. Scrap titanium is a more interesting market, however. This material arises in the form of machine turnings, sheet cuttings or solids. These come mainly from large aircraft manufacturing centres, such as the US, the USSR and West Germany. Prices vary according to the alloy type, form and contamination.

Tungsten

Tungsten ore production, 1977   *thousand metric tons WO₃ content*

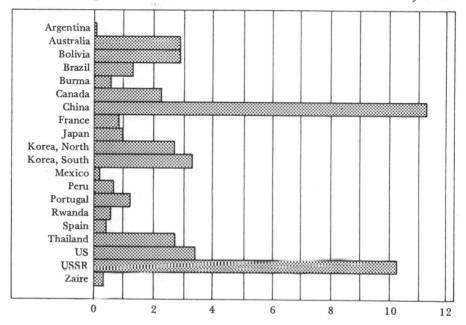

Total world production 49,393 metric tons WO₃ content

Grades available

Tungsten is traded mainly in the intermediate forms of the metal. These are the concentrates, wolframite and scheelite, ferro-tungsten (the alloy of iron and tungsten) and ammonium paratungstate (APT). Pure tungsten, usually in the form of powder, is also traded, but this is a very minor proportion of the business.

Up to 90 per cent of the world's international business in tungsten is conducted in the concentrates. These are traded in metric ton units. One MTU is a single per cent of WO_3 contained in a metric ton of the concentrate, i.e. 22.046 lbs of WO_3. Most commercial grades of tungsten concentrates contain about 65-70 per cent WO_3 which means that they have 65-70 MTU per metric ton.

The concentrates traded are scheelite ($CaWO_4$), ferberite ($FeWO_4$), huebnerite ($MnWO_4$) and wolframite ($[FeMn]WO_4$). Ferberite, huebnerite and wolframite are loosely referred to as wolfram ore or black ore in the trade. Traders pay particular attention to the levels of impurities in these concentrates. The most important of these are tin, arsenic, phosphorus, sulphur, copper and molybdenum. The average scheelite or wolfram ore would contain:

WO_3 (tungsten oxide)	68 per cent
Sn (tin)	0.2 per cent maximum
As (arsenic)	0.2 per cent maximum
P (phosphorus)	0.04 per cent maximum
S (sulphur)	0.5 per cent maximum
Cu (copper)	0.1 per cent maximum
Mo (molybdenum)	0.3 per cent maximum

To confuse the issue further a product called synthetic scheelite is regularly traded which is chemically produced from low grade ores. It is less popular than natural scheelite due mainly to the higher import tariffs it carries into some consumer countries.

Production method

All tungsten concentrates are produced by very simple flotation and gravitational separation from the ore. Ferro-tungsten is either produced by the normal alumino thermic method (reduced from the ore with aluminium powder in the presence of iron) or by reduction in an electric arc furnace. Tungsten scrap is often the feedstock in this last method.

Most pure tungsten is produced in powder form from APT by reduction with hydrogen. APT is produced chemically from the concentrates.

Major uses

There are very many tungsten-containing alloys. Some are steels (scheelite can be used as a direct addition to steel for making many of these alloys) with wide application in all forms of machine tools and mining equipment. Tungsten carbide alloys, made by sintering tungsten powder with other metal powders, also have very wide applications for tools, machinery, components, bullets and tyre studs, etc.

Fine tungsten wire is used for electric lamp filaments, and tungsten metal or alloys are used as contact points in electrical switch gear.

Tungsten compounds are widely used in the chemical industry in lubricants, pigments, catalysts and in many other minor applications.

Main market features

Most of the uses for tungsten are vitally important for the world's industrial activity. Substitution on a large scale with other materials in these uses is very difficult. Fluctuations in demand usually reflect the general state of the world's economic situation, but the price trend in the last two decades has been rising substantially due mainly to the increase in demand and to growing control by tungsten producers.

Tungsten is a typical example of a vitally important raw material which is produced mainly in third world countries but consumed mainly in industrialized countries. It is used widely in the production of armaments and armour plating, and the forecast international increase in expenditure on armaments should ensure a significant increase in demand for tungsten.

China alone produces over a quarter of the world's supply and is in a position to exercise a massive degree of control over prices. The world's producers display a degree of cooperation but the smaller producers in South East Asia and South America rely upon China to set the pace.

With almost no substitution possible and a rising demand, it is reasonable to suppose producers will exert control over supplies to ensure that prices continue to rise, especially as China is expected to increase its internal demand for tungsten over the next decade.

Known world reserves

Reserves of tungsten ore (wolfram content) are approximately 1,200,000 metric tons. 900,000 metric tons are estimated to be in China.

Method of marketing and pricing

The tungsten market, perhaps more than any other, is conducted by international merchants.

It is extremely volatile and very speculative. The purchases from China and the sales to Eastern European countries, including the USSR, are the backbone of the trade. More trade in tungsten is being conducted between China and the USSR these days, however, in spite of some political antagonism between the two countries.

The Chinese conduct a responsible, if somewhat erratic, sales policy. They may withdraw entirely as sellers for long periods of time if they feel the price is too low, only to appear as aggressive sellers when the price suits them or when they have a requirement for foreign currency. Their No 1 grade wolfram ore specification is a standard for world trade.

The other smaller producers have their own specification for their product, and assays usually have to be made by independent assayers on the outturn of cargoes.

With the exception of North America, very few producers sell directly to consumers.

The most authoritative price for the ore is recorded in the London Metal Bulletin, but there is much bitter controversy from producers, consumers and merchants alike concerning the accuracy of these records.

Many efforts have been made to find a more suitable way of international pricing but without success.

In 1978 an International Price Index, using information drawn from both consumers and western world producers, was introduced as a means of reflecting more price influences than just the free market merchant price published by the Metal Bulletin.

Tungsten is an expensive product with a volatile market which has attracted intense speculation, often with dire results for the speculator. Without this speculation, however, it would be difficult to envisage how

Tungsten ore prices (free market)   *US dollars per metric ton unit*

the tungsten market could be conducted.

The General Services Administration (GSA), the American strategic stockpile, retains large stocks of tungsten in various forms. This material is currently made available to buyers in regular official sales. It is an additional confusing ingredient in this very complicated market.

Vanadium

Vanadium ore production, 1977 *thousand metric tons*

Total world production 31,000 metric tons

Grades available

The pure metal is seldom traded, as vanadium additions to steel are usually made in the form of ferro-vanadium. The bulk of trades are in vanadium pentoxide (V_2O_5) or ferro-vanadium usually containing either 80 per cent or 50 per cent vanadium, the balance is iron.

Production method

Although vanadium is a very common metal in the earth's crust, it is only rarely found in commercially viable concentrations, often in association with other ores and minerals.

It is also extracted from the flue dust of power stations which use vanadium rich cokes and coals.

Ores or vanadium-containing slags are converted into vanadium oxide or directly into ferro-vanadium.

The raw material is concentrated, leached and roasted to the oxide.

Ferro-vanadium is usually produced aluminothermically by reduction of the oxide in the presence of aluminium powder and iron.

Major uses

Most vanadium is used in the form of ferro-vanadium in the production of structural steels. An important growth area for such steels is in the manufacture of oil and gas pipelines. The growth in production of pipelines has become particularly marked since the tremendous rise in fuel prices in 1974 and 1975.

There are important uses for such steels in bridge building and high-rise buildings.

Other types of steels containing vanadium are used wherever toughness is required in machinery components, mining equipment and tools.

Certain non-ferrous alloys incorporate a vanadium content, notably some titanium alloys.

Vanadium compounds are used in the chemical industry as catalysts in glazes and for the manufacture of some synthetic rubbers.

Main market features

South Africa produces approximately half the world's vanadium which implies that it should be in a position to exercise a degree of control on the market. Although it is true that the South Africans could set the pace for price changes, they appear to be conscious of the fact that

Ferro-Vanadium prices *£ per kilo V contained*

the other so-called refractory metals, tungsten, molybdenum and niobium, are able to replace vanadium in many of its applications.

This feature of the market perhaps more than any other has kept price movements reasonably gentle.

The current boom in pipeline construction has created an increased demand for vanadium and its competitors which may signal a change in this historic pattern.

Vanadium has been included in the list of strategically important raw materials to be purchased for the new West German strategic stockpile. The decision to include vanadium in this stockpile was probably made on the grounds that its largest source, South Africa, is considered to have a somewhat unstable political future. Such a purchase will help to keep prices high.

Any long-term shortage is likely to tempt the few major vanadium producing countries to flex their market muscles.

Method of marketing and pricing

The influence of merchant activity is only felt in times of shortage. The major producers normally have a good deal of success in controlling prices by using an official producer price when contracting with consumers, often on a long-term basis. When producers decide to or are forced to restrict sales due to increased demand, merchants are ready to trade at a premium to the official price. Other sources of material during these times would come from surplus consumers' stocks and other smaller producers.

Zinc

Zinc slab production, 1978 *hundred thousand metric tons*

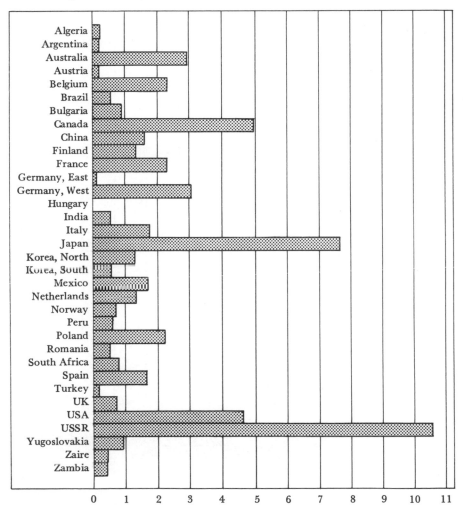

Total world production 6,049,000 metric tons

Zinc slab consumption, 1978

hundred thousand metric tons

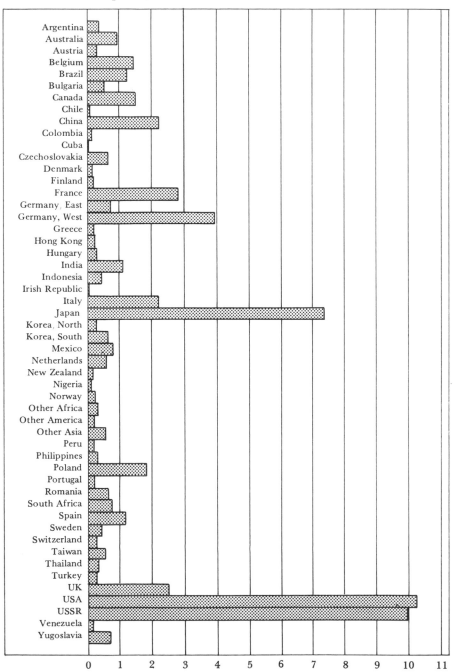

Total world consumption 6,216,000 metric tons

Grades available

The most commonly traded forms of zinc are 'electrolytic' with the purity of 99.95 per cent minimum, 'GOB', standing for good ordinary brand, which is 98.5 per cent minimum, usually debased with lead, and special high grade with the purity greater than 99.99 per cent. All these types are traded in the form of ingots.

Production method

There are a number of different zinc-containing ores but the most commonly commercialized deposits are sulphide ores and the less common oxide ores.

Zinc ores often occur in combination with lead ores and with minor quantities of rarer metals, such as cadmium and indium. These other metals are separated and extracted during the refining process.

The sulphide ore is first roasted to remove sulphur. This sulphur is used to make sulphuric acid which can then be used to dissolve the zinc contained in the ore, to produce zinc sulphate. The zinc in turn is deposited from the solution onto cathodes in the electrolytic refining process. Zinc can also be refined by distillation, where the ore is roasted with carbon and the distillate collected. In both methods the refined metal is cast into slabs.

Major uses

One of zinc's most important uses is in galvanizing, the process of covering steel with a layer of zinc for protection from corrosion. This is commonly used to protect roofing sheets, girders, nails, ladders and buckets etc, and can be achieved by dipping the item in the molten metal or by electrolytic plating. Another major use is in brass, its alloy with copper.

Zinc and zinc alloys are also used extensively to produce die-casting alloys where they compete fiercely with aluminium. Zinc is heavier, but aluminium more costly. Zinc sheet has many uses, the most important being the cases for dry-cell batteries. Zinc oxide is used extensively in the rubber industry and in making white paint and pigments.

Main market features

Zinc is produced mainly in developed countries, notably Canada which is by far the largest producer, although, as with a number of other metals, future supplies are likely to come more from new deposits in the developing world. So far only Peru and Mexico are significant zinc producers in the third world. The Soviet Union is the world's second largest zinc producer and the largest producer in the communist bloc though North Korea and Poland are the major exporters to the Western World. A significant proportion of the world's zinc metal output, however, is concentrated in Western Europe, with smelters using zinc concentrates bought from mine producers. US zinc smelter production, however, has fallen sharply in the past decade, and the country is now far more reliant on imports. Strict anti-pollution regulations introduced by the government have made a number of US smelters uneconomic to operate, and during a period of low prices many of the old fashioned horizontal retort smelters were shut down and have not been replaced. The emphasis in new smelters all over the world is to switch to processes with less pollution. As a result modern smelters are tending to concentrate on zinc output, with by-products, rather than the older smelters producing both lead and zinc taken from the same ore.

An important feature of zinc is that, unlike copper, aluminium and lead, there is only a limited recovery of secondary, or scrap, zinc. This is because the main outlet is in galvanizing steel, requiring only a thin layer which is difficult to recover. However, the growth of the zinc die-casting market has created extra scope for increased scrap recovery, but this forms only a small part of the total market.

Known world reserves

125 million metric tons.

Method of marketing and pricing

The bulk of the non-communist world's zinc mine and metal production is sold under direct supply contracts concluded on an annual basis between producers or smelters and consumers. The tonnage to be supplied is agreed, and the relevant published producer price quotation is used as a pricing basis. There are two main producer price quotations. One, in cents per pound, is used by US and Canadian producers and applies to the North American markets. The other is the so-called European producer price that is used for supply contracts in the rest of the world. Although known as the European price, it is in fact used by producers and smelters throughout the world as a basis for pricing ore concentrates as well as the refined metal.

The producer price for zinc, especially the European quotation, has come under increasing pressure in recent years. Producers and smelters have found it more difficult to cooperate amongst themselves. The mine producers are concerned with the overall return from selling the mine production in the form of ore concentrates, or from their smelters' production of metal. But the independent smelters, unconnected with mining, are only concerned with achieving a profit between the cost of buying in the concentrates and selling the smelted metal. In weak market conditions, therefore, there is pressure by the smelters to reduce the cost of concentrates to maintain their margins, if they are forced to discount the selling price of the smelted metal. But producers are naturally opposed to this reduction in their overall return. The fragile relationship between producers and smelters in a number of countries was further undermined by the threat of anti-cartel action by

Zinc prices (LME cash settlement)

£ per long ton until 1970 and
£ per metric ton from then
onwards — annual average

the US Government and the EEC Commission.

As a result the unofficial producers group was unable to take positive action to protect the European producer price, when a large surplus of supplies developed in 1977 as a result of a slump in demand, that lasted much longer than expected. The producer quotation became a 'nominal' quotation and the real prices being charged were reflected on the London Metal Exchange 'free' zinc market that has assumed a much greater importance. Since most zinc is sold under direct supply contracts, with little passing through the Exchange, prices remain, to a large extent, under the control of producers. In 1978 the producer price was reduced to more realistic levels, production cutbacks were implemented and producer control again asserted over the market. But the earlier virtual collapse of the European producer quotation demonstrated its inability to cope with a changing market situation adequately and brought more interest in the Metal Exchange free market. A zinc futures market on the New York commodity exchange, however, failed to attract much support. Market prices remained under pressure throughout 1979 and early 1980 as a result of declining demand for zinc. This created surplus stocks despite sizeable production cutbacks.

Zirconium

Zirconium ore production, 1977   *thousand metric tons*

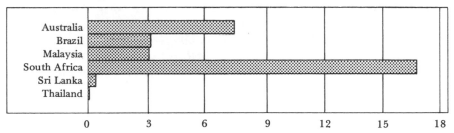

	0	3	6	9	12	15	18

Total world production approx 32,000 metric tons

Grades available

The most common zirconium containing substances are its alloys, some of which are known as zircaloy, containing small quantities of tin or tin with iron, chrome and nickel. Zirconium metal is usually sold in the form of sponge and ingot.

Production method

Zirconium's ore, zircon, is roasted with coke in an electric arc furnace which produces zirconium carbonitride. This is then chlorinated to produce the chloride which is in turn reacted with magnesium metal to produce zirconium metal.

Major uses

Zircon, the ore, has a major use in its own right for making foundry moulding sands.

Several zirconium compounds have uses for making waxes, tanning agents, rust and water repellents, and deodorants.

The alloys have uses in the manufacture of pipes, pumps, valves and fittings in the chemical industry where their anti-corrosion properties are required.

Some pure metal is used in the construction of components for nuclear reactors and for making foil used in flash bulbs.

Main market features

Zirconium is produced by very few manufacturers. Its raw material is plentiful and very little of it is used to produce the metal. It is rather expensive to produce when one considers that another metal, magnesium, is required to make it. Its price has been rising steadily over the years in line with production costs. The price of its rather inexpensive ore, however, has been changing somewhat more erratically due to the changing fortunes in the markets of its non-metallic uses. This all makes the market rather unexciting for metal merchants who confine their activity to trading in the ore or the scrap alloy.

No drastic upsurge in demand is foreseen but a major expansion in nuclear plant construction could cause a temporary lack of production capacity.

Method of marketing and pricing

The few manufacturers that there are sell directly to consumers. They also offer a range of alloys and in most cases semi-fabricated products as well. These producers determine what price they can charge and competition between them is not particularly fierce.

Zirconium ore prices   *£ per metric ton*

Appendices

Appendix 1:
Glossary of relevant terms

Actuals: Physical commodities, also commodities readily available. The commodity itself as opposed to a futures contract

Agent: A merchant who acts on behalf of a producer usually on a commission basis

Anode: The electrode at which negatively charged ions are discharged during electrolysis

Arbitrage: Purchase of contract in one market while simultaneously selling the same amount in another to take advantage of price differentials

Backwardation: Market description of the situation when the spot or nearby prices are higher than those for future delivery months. Usually caused by delays in shipment thus creating shortages in available supplies. Opposite of contango

Basic price: Agreed price between buyer and seller of an option at which the option may be taken up. Also called the 'striking price'

Bear: Person expecting a decline in prices

Bear covering: Closing of short positions

Bid: The price which the buyer is willing to pay

Borrowing: Purchase of a nearby delivery date and simultaneous sale of a forward date. Used only in London Metal Exchange

Brine: Solution of any salt

Broker: Establishes contact between buyer and seller, for a fee. In the US, ring dealing members of futures markets are frequently called brokers

Bulk: Delivery of unpacked metal

Bull: Person expecting a rise in prices

Call: A period for trading. Conducted by a chairman to establish a price for a specific time. During a call, trading is confined to one delivery month

Call option: The option buyer/taker pays a premium and holds the right to decide at a later stage whether or not to buy at the price agreed at the time the premium was paid. The right may be exercised at any time from the point of purchase to the expiry of the option

Carrying: General term covering both *Borrowing* and *Lending*

Carrying Costs: Costs connected with warehouse storage, insurance, etc. On occasion includes interest and estimated changes in weight

Casting: Metal object made by pouring molten metal into a mould, which does not involve mechanical work such as rolling or forging

Catalyst: A chemical (metal) which assists a chemical reaction but remains chemically unchanged at the end

Cathode: The electrode at which positively charged (metallic) ions are discharged during electrolysis, hence the slab of metal deposited at the end of the electrolytic process

Certified stocks: Supplies rates as deliverable

C&F: Cost and freight

CIF: Cost, insurance and freight (included in price)

Clearing house: The organization that provides clearing facilities for some futures markets

Commission house: A company, which trades on behalf of clients for a commission. The Commission House only handles clients' business and does not trade on its own account

Concentrate: The ore of a metal after separation from other unwanted minerals

Conductivity: A measure of the ability of a metal to conduct an electric current

Contango: A situation where prices are higher in the forward delivery months than in the nearby delivery month. Opposite of backwardation. Normally in evidence when supplies are adequate or in surplus. The contango reflects either wholly or in part the costs of holding and financing

Contract: An agreement to buy or sell a specified amount of a particular commodity. It details the amount and grade of the product and the date on which the contract will mature and become deliverable, if not previously liquidated

Contract month: Month in which a given contract becomes deliverable, if not liquidated or traded out before the date specified

Custom smelter: A smelter which relies on concentrate purchased from independent mines instead of its own captive sources

Delivery basis: Specified locations to which the commodity in a futures contract may be physically delivered in order to terminate the contract

Delivery date: Or Prompt Date, on which the commodity must be delivered to fulfil the terms of the contract

Delivery month: Calendar month stipulated as month of delivery in a futures contract

Deposit: Sum of money required by the broker from his client, usually 10 per cent of the value of the contract, to justify opening of a futures position

Differentials: Premiums paid for grades better than the basic grade, or discounts allowed for grades below the basic grade

Double option: This is an option which gives the buyer or person taking the option the right either to buy from or sell to the seller of the option or the person who gives it, at the strike price

Ductility: Quality of a metal by which it may be beaten into sheet or drawn into a wire

Electrolysis: A process used for refining metals where the metal is deposited on a cathode from a solution or molten mass

Element: A substance which cannot be split into anything simpler in a chemical process

Fabricator: A company which makes semi-fabricated products from refined metal and on occasions from scrap

Fixation: Fixing price in the future, and used in commodity call purchases and call sale trades

Flotation: Process by which ore is separated from earth and rubble, during which the ore is introduced to a bath of liquid which is agitated so that the metallic ore either rises to the top or sinks to the bottom

Flux: A substance added to a metal in order to make it easier to melt

FOB: Free on Board

Force Majeure: This is a clause in a supply contract which permits either party not to fulfil the contractual commitments due to events beyond their control. These events may range from strikes to export delays in producing countries

Forward shipment: Contract covering actual commodity shipments at a specified date in the future

Futures contract: Contract which requires the delivery of a commodity in a specified future month, if not liquidated before the contract matures

Grades: Standards set for judging the quality of a commodity

Hedge: A temporary futures market sale which is made against a spot purchase, or alternatively a temporary futures market purchase made against a spot sale. The purpose is to reduce risk from price fluctuations on the physical transaction until the reverse futures market operation cancels the hedge, or liquidates the original operation

Inorganic: Compounds other than those of carbon, but including the oxides of carbon and carbonates

Integrated producer: A producer who owns mines, smelters and refineries and also, in some instances, fabricating plants

Kerb trading: Unofficial trading when the market has closed. The term 'kerb' dates from the time when dealers continued trading on the kerb outside the exchanges after these had closed

Last trading day: Final day for trading a particular delivery. Positions which have not been closed by the last trading day must be fulfilled by making, or taking, delivery of the physical commodity or metal

Leaching: The process by which metals are extracted from a low grade ore or waste product, by the direct action of a caustic solution or an acid, producing a metallic salt solution

Lending: Sale of a nearby delivery date coupled with the simultaneous purchase of a more distant date (LME term)

Limit up/down: Largest permitted rise/fall in the price of a commodity traded in a futures contract during a trading session, as fixed by the contract market's rules

Liquidation: Sale of long contract to offset previous purchase. Operation which cancels an earlier position

Long: An open purchased futures contract. Buying forward on the market

Lot: Minimum contract unit in a hedge or futures market

Margin: This is the amount deposited as a guarantee for the fluctuations on a futures purchase or sale. If the contract fluctuates against the holder of the contract, he is required to provide for the difference between his contract price and the current market price by paying 'variation margin' differences. Thus the original margin continues to guarantee fully the performance of the contract at any market price level

Margin call: A commodity broker's request to a client for additional funds to secure the original deposits

Master alloy: An alloy made with two metals x and y, which is then added to a larger quantity of metal x so that metal y is diluted to the required proportion

Nearby delivery: The nearest active month of delivery on a futures market

Offer: The seller's price for the commodity offered

Open contracts: Contracts bought or sold and not offset by an opposite trade

Open outcry: Trading conducted by calling out bids and offers across a ring or pit and having them accepted

Open position: A forward market position which has not been closed out

Option: The holder of the option has the right to buy from or sell to the granter of the option a specified quantity of the commodity at an agreed price. The cost of buying the option is known as the premium

Pegged price: The price at which a commodity has been fixed by agreement

Plating: The deposition of a layer of a metal on an object forming the cathode during electrolysis

Position trader: Someone who takes long or short positions in futures markets in consequence of an opinion that prices are about to advance or decline

Premium: The amount by which a cash commodity price sells over a futures price or another cash commodity price. The excess of one futures contract price over another

Put option: This option gives the buyer (or 'taker') of the option — in exchange for the premium which he pays — the right to decide at a later date whether or not to sell to the seller (or 'granter') at the price ('basic' or 'striking' price) agreed at the time the premium was paid. The right may be exercised at any point from the purchase of the option up to the declaration date (the date upon which the option expires)

Reduction: A process involving the removal of oxygen or a group which forms negative ions

Ring: Space on a trading floor where futures are traded. Also known as a pit in the US

Roast: Heating ore or concentrate in air or inert atmosphere to extract unwanted element, usually sulphur

Salt: A compound containing a metal and a non-metal

Scavenger: Substance added to molten metal which has the effect of ridding the melt of an unwanted element

Semi-fabrication: The production of metal in the form of wire, sheet, rod etc

Short: The sale of a commodity not owned by the seller

Slime: Substance containing metal other than that deposited at the cathode during electrolysis and which is found as a sludge in the bottom of the electrolytic cell

Smelt: Extraction of crude metal from the ore by melting, prior to refining

Sponge: Lumpy form of metal with sponge-like appearance produced by casting molten metal into water

Spot: Term denoting immediate delivery for cash, as distinct from future delivery

Spot month: The first month in which delivery can take place and for which a quotation is made on the futures market

Spot price: The commodity cash sale price, as opposed to a futures price

Spread: An order to purchase one contract month and sell another month in the same commodity, usually done on the same exchange

Squeeze: Pressure on a delivery date which results in the price of that date becoming firmer in relation to other dates

Straddle: The simultaneous buying and selling of the same commodity on the same market. This is designed to take advantage of differences between two options. Example — the sale of a September option and the simultaneous purchase of a January option made in the expectation that a later simultaneous purchase of the September and sale of the January options will produce a profit. See *Arbitrage*

Sublimation: Heating an unrefined metal until it turns into its gaseous form. This is then condensed into the refined metal

Switch: To advance or postpone the original contract to a different month

Switching: Exchanging a commodity in one warehouse for a commodity in another

Terminal market: Usually synonymous with commodity exchange or futures market, especially in the United Kingdom

Unwrought: Metal in a cast condition, unworked by mechanical means

Warehouse receipt: A receipt for a commodity given by a licensed or authorized warehouseman and issued as tender on futures contracts

Warrant or Warehouse receipt: A receipt of physical deposit which gives title to the physical commodity

Appendix 2:

Average monthly dollar/sterling rate based on the market price at 11.30 a.m. each dealing day

	January	February	March	April	May	June	July	August	September	October	November	December	Average
1958	2.8000	2.8000	2.8000	2.8000	2.8000	2.7999	2.7979	2.7978	2.7981	2.7980	2.7995	2.7994	2.7992
1959	2.8047	2.8077	2.8103	2.8148	2.8127	2.8109	2.8101	2.8080	2.8020	2.8050	2.8012	2.7970	2.8070
1960	2.7985	2.8017	2.8041	2.8078	2.8046	2.8010	2.8065	2.8084	2.8107	2.8096	2.8119	2.8057	2.8059
1961	2.8047	2.7986	2.7956	2.7965	2.7922	2.7888	2.7854	2.8006	2.8096	2.8136	2.8130	2.8078	2.8005
1962	2.8089	2.8126	2.8132	2.8122	2.8105	2.8068	2.8050	2.8023	2.7995	2.7999	2.8001	2.8019	2.8061
1963	2.8031	2.8018	2.7990	2.7990	2.7980	2.7986	2.7993	2.7981	2.7961	2.7964	2.7964	2.7951	2.7984
1964	2.7967	2.7955	2.7966	2.7974	2.7979	2.7926	2.7884	2.7852	2.7819	2.7820	2.7833	2.7887	2.7905
1965	2.7895	2.7932	2.7904	2.7933	2.7953	2.7904	2.7892	2.7891	2.7945	2.8014	2.8020	2.8003	2.7941
1966	2.8025	2.8010	2.7938	2.7913	2.7908	2.7884	2.7873	2.7875	2.7877	2.7901	2.7896	2.7884	2.7916
1967	2.7892	2.7924	2.7943	2.7974	2.7952	2.7899	2.7860	2.7838	2.7829	2.7817	2.6430	2.4062	2.7452
1968	2.4087	2.4094	2.3992	2.4015	2.3891	2.3845	2.3892	2.3912	2.3869	2.3895	2.3874	2.3838	2.3934
1969	2.3866	2.3910	2.3913	2.3928	2.3862	2.3896	2.3902	2.3855	2.3837	2.3896	2.3962	2.3967	2.3900
1970	2.3999	2.4042	2.4056	2.4059	2.4033	2.3976	2.3903	2.3877	2.3845	2.3870	2.3899	2.3903	2.3955
1971	2.4047	2.4170	2.4182	2.4175	2.4183	2.4179	2.4182	2.4342	2.4709	2.4915	2.4937	2.5267	2.4441
1972	2.5703	2.6030	2.6178	2.6093	2.6117	2.5814	2.4415	2.4502	2.4425	2.3968	2.3518	2.3456	2.5018
1973	2.3558	2.4418	2.4778	2.4825	2.5174	2.5743	2.5402	2.4742	2.4163	2.4260	2.3890	2.3171	2.4510
1974	2.2263	2.2738	2.3369	2.3906	2.4117	2.3876	2.3869	2.3445	2.3146	2.3310	2.3271	2.3271	2.3382
1975	2.3603	2.3917	2.4172	2.3680	2.3185	2.2807	2.1833	2.1133	2.0852	2.0548	2.0499	2.0208	2.2203
1976	2.0276	2.0257	1.9455	1.8476	1.8156	1.7710	1.7863	1.7819	1.7309	1.6401	1.6370	1.6787	1.8073
1977	1.7127	1.7100	1.7172	1.7195	1.7188	1.7193	1.7221	1.7403	1.7436	1.7703	1.8203	1.8550	1.7458
1978	1.9338	1.9405	1.9103	1.8507	1.8175	1.8366	1.8940	1.9419	1.9593	1.9740	1.9905	1.9950	1.9203
1979	2.0030	2.0040	2.0351	2.0759	2.0541	2.1029	2.2495	2.2326	2.2005	2.1472	2.1308	2.1966	2.1190
1980	2.2676	2.2908	2.1982	2.2146	2.2913								

Appendix 3:

Standard Times at noon Greenwich Mean Time

British Summer Time, which is one hour ahead of GMT, is observed from 02.00 hours on the third Sunday in March until 02.00 on the fourth Sunday in October. USA Daylight Saving Time, which is one hour ahead of local standard time, is observed in all states except Arizona, Hawaii and Michigan from 02.00 on the last Sunday in April until 02.00 on the last Sunday in October. In France, in 1977, Summer Time, which is also one hour ahead of local standard time, is observed from 24.00 hours on 3 April to 24.00 on 25 September.

City	Time	City	Time	City	Time
Accra	12.00	Damascus	14.00	Ottawa	07.00
Adelaide	21.30	Darwin	21.30	Panama	07.00
Algiers	13.00	Delhi	17.30	Paris	13.00
Amman	14.00	Djakarta	20.00	Peking	20.00
Amsterdam	13.00	Dublin	12.00	Perth	20.00
Ankara	14.00	Gibraltar	13.00	Prague	13.00
Athens	14.00	Helsinki	14.00	Quebec	07.00
Auckland	24.00	Hobart	22.00	Rangoon	18.30
Baghdad	15.00	Hong Kong	20.00	Rawalpindi	17.00
Bangkok	19.00	Istanbul	14.00	Reykjavik	12.00
Beirut	14.00	Jerusalem	14.00	Rio de Janeiro	09.00
Belgrade	13.00	Karachi	17.00	Rome	13.00
Berlin	13.00	Kuala Lumpur	20.00	San Francisco	04.00
Berne	13.00	Lagos	13.00	Santiago	08.00
Bombay	17:30	Leningrad	15.00	Sofia	14.00
Bonn	13.00	Lima	07.00	Singapore	19.30
Brisbane	22.00	Lisbon	13.00	Stockholm	13.00
Brussels	13.00	Luxembourg	13.00	Sydney	22.00
Bucharest	14.00	Madras	17.30	Tehran	15.30
Budapest	13.00	Madrid	13.00	Tokyo	21.00
Buenos Aires	09.00	Melbourne	22.00	Toronto	07.00
Cairo	14.00	Mexico City	06.00	Tunis	13.00
Calcutta	17.30	Montevideo	08.30	Vancouver	04.00
Canberra	22.00	Moscow	15.00	Vienna	13.00
Cape Town	14.00	Nairobi	15.00	Warsaw	13.00
Caracas	08.00	New York	07.00	Washington	07.00
Chicago	06.00	Nicosia	14.00	Wellington	24.00
Copenhagen	13.00	Oslo	13.00	Winnipeg	06.00

Note to World Time Zones map
The earth turns one complete revolution in 24 hours. The surface of the Earth is divided into 24 Time Zones, each of $15°$ longitude or 1 hour of time. In 24 hours it turns through $360°$. The times shown are the standard times on land and sea when it is 12.00 hours on the Greenwich Meridian.

World Time Zones

Appendix 4:
London Metal Exchange contract rules and arbitration

CONTRACTS

Rule A

Members of the London Metal Exchange, in their dealings with other Members, shall be responsible to and entitled to claim against one another, and one another only, for the fulfilment of every Contract for Metals.

Rule B

In these Rules the expression "Members of the London Metal Exchange" includes Firms and Companies who, although not themselves Subscribers to the Exchange, are represented and deal thereon by and through "Representative Subscribers" to the Exchange acting as the representatives or Agents of such Firms or Companies.

Rule C

If any Member of the Metal Exchange fails to meet his engagements to another Member, whether by failing to provide on the due date documents (i.e. Bills of Lading, Warrants or Delivery Orders according to the metals dealt in) to meet sales made or money to pay for metals bought, or by making default in fulfilling any other obligation arising out of dealings made subject to the Rules and Regulations of the London Metal Exchange, notice of the default shall be given at once in writing to the Committee of the Exchange and the Committee shall immediately fix and publish a settlement price or prices as at the date of such communication to them for all contracts which the defaulter may have open under these Rules, whether with Members or with parties who are not Members. All such contracts shall forthwith be closed and balanced, by selling to or buying from the defaulting Member such metals as he may have contracted to deliver or take, at the settlement prices fixed for this purpose by the Committee, and any difference arising whether from or to the party in default shall become payable forthwith notwithstanding that the prompt day or other day originally stipulated for the settlement of the transaction may not have arrived. In fixing settlement prices under this Rule the Committee may in their discretion take into consideration the extent and nature of the transactions which the defaulting Member has open and any other circumstance which they may consider should affect their decision. In any case where the Committee shall be of opinion that the default is not due to the insolvency of the defaulter the Committee shall by resolution negative the application of this rule. Any claim arising out of a default not due to insolvency shall be settled by arbitration in the usual manner. This rule shall apply to cases in which at or after the decease of a Member the engagements entered into by him are not duly met.

Rule D

In any Contract made subject to the Rules and Regulations of the London Metal Exchange between a Member and a Non-Member in the event of the Non-Member failing to meet his engagements arising out of any such contract whether by failing to provide on the due date documents to meet sales or money to take up documents (as the case may be) or otherwise howsoever or of his failing to supply or maintain such margin (if any) for which the Member is entitled to call and has called, or in the event of the Non-Member's suspending payment or becoming bankrupt or committing any act of bankruptcy or (being a Company) in the event of its going into liquidation whether voluntary or otherwise, the Member shall have the right to close all or any such Contracts outstanding between them by selling out or buying in against the Non-Member (as the case may be) and any differences arising therefrom shall be payable forthwith notwithstanding that the prompt day or other day originally stipulated for settlement may not have arrived.

Rule E
Payments for Warrants or other documents (when deliverable under the Contracts) unless otherwise stipulated on the Contract, shall be made by cash in London, or by cheque on a London clearing bank, either mode in Seller's option. The documents shall be tendered in London against the cash or cheque, as the case may be, and not later than 2.30 p.m. on the prompt or settling day.

Rule F
Contracts wherein Buyer or Seller (as the case may be) has the option to uplift or to deliver, prior to the prompt or settlement date by giving previous notice of his intention, shall have the notice reckoned by market days; such notices, unless otherwise stipulated at time of purchase or sale, shall be as follows: On a Contract with the option to uplift or to deliver during one calendar month or less, one day's notice shall be given; on a Contract with the option beyond one and up to two calendar months two days' notice shall be given; and on a Contract with the option beyond two and up to three calendar months three days' notice shall be given previous to the date on which delivery is required, or will be made. Notice shall be given for the whole quantity stated in the contract and shall be tendered in writing and delivered at the office of the Seller of the option not later than noon on the day of notice. Rent shall only be allowed to Buyer to actual day of settlement; and there shall not be any allowance of interest for a payment made prior to the prompt date.

Rule G
Prompt or settlement dates falling on Saturday, Sunday, or a Bank Holiday, which days are not market days, shall be settled as follows: Prompts falling on Saturday shall be settled on the Friday previous; but should the preceding Friday be a Bank Holiday the prompt shall be extended to the Monday following; should both the Friday preceding and the Monday following be Bank Holidays, the prompt shall be settled on the Thursday previous. Prompts falling on Sunday should be extended to the Monday following, but should that Monday be a Bank Holiday the prompt shall be extended to the Tuesday following; should both the following Monday and Tuesday be Bank Holidays, the prompt shall then be extended to the Wednesday following. Prompts falling on a Bank Holiday shall be extended to the day following; and if the Bank Holiday falls on Friday the prompt shall be extended to the Monday following; but should the Friday be Good Friday, prompts falling on that day shall be settled on the Thursday previous. If Christmas Day falls on Monday, prompts falling on that day shall be extended to the Wednesday following, but if Christmas Day falls on Tuesday, Wednesday, Thursday or Friday, prompts falling on that day shall be settled on the day previous.

Rule H
The establishment, or attempted establishment of a "corner", or participation directly or indirectly in either, being detrimental to the interests of the Exchange, the Committee shall, if in their opinion a "corner" has been or is in the course of being established, have power to investigate the matter and to take whatever action it considers proper to restore equilibrium between supply and demand. Any member or members may be required to give such information as is in his or their possession relative to the matter under investigation.

Rule J (OPTIONS)
On the day on which notice is due, the holder of the option shall, except in cases to which Rule C applies, declare in writing before 11.30 a.m. whether he exercises or abandons the option, and if he fails to make such declaration the option shall be considered as abandoned. Options (subject to Rule F above) may be declared for less than the total optional quantity in quantities of 25 tonnes for Copper-Electrolytic Wirebars, H.C.F.R. Wirebars, Cathodes or Fire Refined, 5 tonnes for Standard Tin, High Grade Tin, 25 tonnes for Aluminium, 10,000 troy ounces for Silver, and 6 tonnes for Nickel, or multiples thereof, only one declaration against each contract being allowed. In cases to which Rule C applies the prices fixed by the Committee, at which outstanding contracts are to be closed, shall equally apply to all option contracts; and all options shall be automatically determined, and be deemed to have been either exercised or abandoned according as the prices may be in favour of or against the defaulter and whether the defaulter be the Seller or the Buyer of an option, and the option money shall be brought into account. In contracts with optional prompts, the price which shall be taken as the basis of settlement shall be the settlement price fixed by the Committee under Rule C for the prompt most favourable to the holder of the option.

Rule K (CLEARING)
All contracts made between Members of the London Metal Exchange who are entitled to deal in the Ring, either for Copper-Electrolytic Wirebars, H.C.F.R. Wirebars, Cathodes or Fire Refined, Standard Tin, High Grade Tin, Standard Lead, Standard Zinc, Aluminium, Nickel or Silver, shall be settled through the Clearing, except when a Member insists on his right to receive cash instead of cheque from the Member to whom he has sold, in which case the Seller shall give notice to his Buyer before noon on the market day preceding the settling day, and such transactions shall then be exempted from settlement through the Clearing. The Rules governing the Clearing of all contracts shall be those in existence at the time fixed for the fulfilment of the contract. Copies of such rules may be obtained from the Secretary of the Exchange.

Rule L
In case of strikes, lock-outs, or other unforeseen contingencies in London, or other authorised port or point of delivery, which prevent or delay the discharge and/or warehousing of Copper-Electrolytic Wirebars, H.C.F.R. Wirebars, Cathodes or Fire Refined, Standard Tin, High Grade Tin, Standard Lead, Standard Zinc, Aluminium, Nickel and/or Silver, the Seller may be allowed to postpone delivery if he can prove to the satisfaction of the Committee (of which proof the Committee shall be the sole judge) that he does not hold available metal in warehouse or vault with which to fulfil his contracts and that he has metal of the requisite quality which has arrived in London or any other authorised port or point of delivery at least ten days prior to the earliest prompt for which relief is asked, or has metal of the requisite quality in his works, but the delivery, discharge and/or other warehousing of which is prevented or delayed as aforesaid. He must also deposit with the Secretary of the

Exchange such sums as the Committee may require but not exceeding £5 per tonne in the case of Copper, Lead, Zinc and Aluminium, £10 per tonne in the case of Tin and Primary Nickel, and £5 per thousand ounces in the case of Silver. No interest will be allowed on deposits, which will be returned after delivery of Warrants. Should his application be passed by the Committee, he shall deposit documents or other proof to the satisfaction of the Committee with the Secretary of the Exchange, who shall issue Certificates for Copper, Lead, Zinc and Aluminium in quantities of 25 tonnes, Certificates for Nickel in quantities of 6 tonnes, Certificates for Tin in quantities of 5 tonnes, and Certificates for Silver in quantities of 10,000 troy ounces. The Seller shall deliver these Certificates to his Buyer. The Certificates will then constitute a good delivery on the Clearing within the period stated thereon and differences must be settled on the prompt day. The holder of a Certificate must present it to the firm named thereon not later than 2.30 p.m. on the day following that on which he receives notice in writing from his Seller that the Warrant for the actual Copper, Tin, Lead, Zinc, Aluminium, Nickel or Silver is ready. He must take up the Warrant against payment at the settlement price fixed on the preceding market day, receiving or paying any difference between this and the price mentioned on the Certificate. In the event of the price on the Certificate being above or below the settlement price operative on the day of delivery the receiver shall pay or be paid the amount of any difference. No other payments shall pass except against delivery of the actual Warrant. In case of any dispute, the Committee's ruling to be final. A fee of £5 to be paid by the Applicants for each Certificate issued.

ARBITRATION

Rule 1
All disputes arising out of or in relation to contracts subject to the Rules and Regulations of the London Metal Exchange shall be referred to arbitration as hereinafter provided. The Executive Secretary of the Committee of the London Metal Exchange (hereinafter referred to as "the Secretary") shall be notified of such disputes in writing and the party first notifying the difference shall at the time of such notification deposit with the Metal Market & Exchange Co. Ltd., the sum of £100. All such disputes shall be referred to two arbitrators, one to be appointed by each party to the difference from the Arbitration Panel of the London Metal Exchange, such arbitrators having power to appoint a third arbitrator from the Panel and having all the powers conferred on arbitrators by the Arbitration Act 1950 or any statutory modifications thereof for the time being in force. The Secretary shall be notified in writing by each party of the appointment of the arbitrators. The arbitration and any Appeal made pursuant to Rule 8 of these Rules from the Award of the Arbitrators to the Committee shall take place at the London Metal Exchange (unless mutually agreed by the Arbitrators and the parties to the dispute that the venue should be elsewhere in England or Wales) and English procedure and law shall be applied thereto.

Rule 2
Persons eligible for appointment to the Arbitration Panel shall be members of the Exchange, their partners or co-directors (as the case may be) or members of their staff. Appointment to and removal from the Panel shall be made, at their sole discretion, by the Committee of the London Metal Exchange who will also be responsible for maintaining a panel of sufficient size.

Rule 3
In the event of either party to the difference (a) failing to appoint an arbitrator, or (b) failing to give notice in writing or by cable of such appointment to reach the

other party within 14 days after receiving written or cabled notice from such other party of the appointment of an arbitrator (any notice by either party being given to the other either by cable or by registered post addressed to the usual place of business of such other party), or (c) in the case of death, refusal to act, or incapacity of an arbitrator, then, upon written or cabled request of either party an arbitrator shall be appointed from the said Arbitration Panel by the Committee of the London Metal Exchange.

Rule 4
In case the two arbitrators appointed as aforesaid, whether originally or by way of substitution, shall not within three calendar months after the appointment of the arbitrator last appointed deliver their Award in writing, or choose a third arbitrator, then the said Committee on the written request of either party shall appoint a third arbitrator selected from the said Arbitration Panel to act with the two aforesaid arbitrators.

Rule 5
The Award in writing of the arbitrators or any two of them shall be made and delivered in triplicate to the Secretary within a period of three calendar months from the date of the acceptance of the appointment by the arbitrator last appointed.

Rule 6
Every Award made pursuant to any provision of this Rule shall be conclusive and binding on the parties to the arbitration, subject to appeal as hereinafter mentioned.

Rule 7
The procedure upon an arbitration shall be as follows:

(a) Within a period of 21 days after the appointment of the second of the two arbitrators so appointed, each party shall deliver to the arbitrators and to each other a statement of case in writing with the originals, or copies, of any documents referred to therein. All such documents to be in the English language or accompanied by certified translations into English.

(b) If either party shall make default in delivering such statements and documents (due consideration being given to time occupied by mails), the arbitrators shall proceed with the case on the statement before them, provided always that, in the sole discretion of the arbitrators, an extension of time may be allowed for the delivery of such statements and documents.

(c) The arbitrators shall appoint a day for a hearing within 28 days, or such further time as the arbitrators shall in their sole discretion allow, after the expiry of the 21 days in accordance with Rule 7 (a), and shall give due notice in writing thereof to the parties, who may, and if required by the arbitrators shall, attend and shall submit to examination by the arbitrators and produce such books and documents as the arbitrators may require. Each party shall be entitled to produce verbal evidence before the arbitrators.

(d) Neither Counsel, nor Solicitor shall be briefed to appear for either party without the consent of the arbitrators.

(e) The arbitrators may engage legal or other assistance.

(f) The arbitrators may adjourn the hearing from time to time, giving due notice in writing to the parties of the resumed hearing, and the arbitrators may, if they think fit, proceed with such a resumed hearing in the absence of either party or of both parties.

(g) Where any change takes place in the constitution of the tribunal of arbitrators, either by substitution or otherwise, the new tribunal shall appoint a day for the hearing which shall be not later than 28 days, nor earlier than 7 days, after the change. Each party, if desiring to do so, may submit an Amended Statement of Case, with a copy to the other party, which must reach the new tribunal within seven days of its appointment.

(h) In the event of a third arbitrator being appointed, the provisions contained in Section 9 Sub-Section 1 of the Arbitration Act 1950 shall not apply to any reference.

(i) The cost of the arbitration shall be at the sole discretion of the arbitrators. The arbitrators shall fix the amount of their remuneration. The Award shall state separately the amount of such costs and remuneration and by whom they shall be paid and whether the whole or any part of the deposit referred to in Rule 1 of these Rules shall be returned to the party lodging the same or be forfeited. In the event of either or both parties having been granted permission by the arbitrators to be legally represented at the hearing the arbitrators may take into consideration any legal costs which have been incurred.

(j) The Award shall be deposited with the Secretary who shall forthwith give notice of receipt thereof in writing to both parties, and a copy of such Award shall be delivered to both parties on payment by either party of the costs specified in the Award, which payment shall not affect any provision of the Award.

(k) In the event that after the deposit referred to in Rule 1 of these Rules has been made the parties to the arbitration shall (i) settle their differences (ii) fail to proceed as directed by the arbitrators under sub-clause (c) of this Rule (iii) fail to take up the Award within 28 clear days of notification being given under sub-clause (j) of this Rule, such deposit shall be forfeited.

(l) At the time of issuing their Award, all statements and all documents lodged with the arbitrators shall be delivered by them to the Secretary, by whom they shall be retained until the expiration of the time for giving notice of appeal, as hereinafter mentioned, after which the Secretary shall, unless there shall be such appeal, return them to the parties concerned.

Rule 8
Either party shall have the right to appeal against the Award to the Committee of the London Metal Exchange.

Rule 9
The method of appeal against the Award shall be as follows:

(a) The party making the appeal shall (i) within 21 days of the date of the Award give notice in writing of such appeal to the Secretary, and to the other party and shall at the same time state the grounds for appeal. (ii) Deposit with the Metal Market & Exchange Co. Ltd. the sum of £200, and in addition the sum, if any, which shall be payable under the Award by the Appellant.

(b) Upon receipt of such Notice of Appeal the Committee shall within 4 weeks nominate not less than five members, (hereinafter called "the Appeal Committee") to hear the Appeal. Members of the Appeal Committee shall be members of the Committee of the London Metal Exchange and/or members of the Board of the Metal Market & Exchange Co. Ltd.

(c) The procedure on appeal shall as far as possible be similar to that above provided for the original hearing except that all statements and documents delivered to the Secretary under Rule 7 (l) shall be laid before the Appeal Committee who may, however, require such further statement or statements or other information or documents from either or both of the parties as the Appeal Committee may think necessary. The provisions of Rule 7 (k) shall apply in like manner to the deposit referred to in sub-paragraph (a) (ii) of this Rule as the deposit in connection with the original hearing.

(d) The decision in writing of the majority of the Appeal Committee (which latter shall not at any time number less than five) shall be final and binding on all parties, and the Appeal Committee shall also decide whether the whole or any part of the said deposit of £200 shall be returned to the Appellant or be forfeited.

(e) The Appeal Committee shall have the same discretion regarding costs as is given to the arbitrators under Section 7 (i) and shall fix the amount of their remuneration and direct by whom it shall be paid.

(f) All statements and all documents lodged with the Appeal Committee shall, together with the Award, be deposited by them with the Secretary by whom they shall be retained until the costs and fees specified in the Award have been paid by either party. On payment, which shall not affect any provision of the Award, a copy of the Award shall be delivered to both parties and all documents returned to the parties concerned.

Appendix 5:

Conversion table

Mass	Metric ton	Long ton	Short ton	Pounds	Kilograms	Ounce troy	Grains	Pennyweight	Pikul
Metric ton		0.984	1.102	2204.5	1000				16.535
Long ton	1.016		1.120	2240	1016				
Short ton	0.907	0.893		2000	907				15.000
Pound	0.0004	0.0004	0.0005		0.4536	14.583	7000		
Kilogram	0.001			2.2045		32.150			
Ounce troy							480	20	
Grain						480			
Pennyweight							24		
Pikul	0.0605		0.067	133.33	60.48				

Appendix 6:

Conversion of US metal prices from cents per lb to sterling pounds per metric ton* at varying exchange rates

Metal price: cents per lb	Exchange rate: US dollar/£ sterling									
	1.60	1.70	1.80	1.90	2.00	2.10	2.20	2.30	2.40	2.50
					£ sterling per metric ton					
1	13.77	12.96	12.24	11.60	11.02	10.49	10.01	9.58	9.18	8.81
5	68.85	64.80	61.20	58.00	55.10	52.45	50.05	47.91	45.91	44.08
10	137.70	129.60	122.40	116.00	110.20	104.90	100.10	95.82	91.83	88.16
20	275.40	259.20	244.80	232.00	220.40	209.80	200.20	191.64	183.66	176.32
30	413.10	388.80	367.20	348.00	330.60	314.70	300.30	287.46	275.49	264.48
40	550.80	518.40	489.60	464.00	440.80	419.60	400.40	383.28	367.32	352.64
50	688.50	648.00	612.00	580.00	551.00	524.50	500.50	479.10	459.15	440.80
60	826.20	777.60	734.40	696.00	661.20	629.40	600.60	574.92	550.98	528.96
70	963.90	907.20	856.80	812.00	771.40	734.30	700.70	670.74	642.81	617.12
80	1,101.60	1,036.80	979.20	928.00	881.60	839.20	800.80	766.56	734.64	705.28
90	1,239.30	1,166.40	1,101.60	1,044.00	991.80	944.10	900.90	862.38	826.47	793.44
100	1,377.00	1,296.00	1,224.00	1,160.00	1,102.00	1,049.00	1,001.00	958.20	918.30	881.60

*metric ton = 2,204 lb

Appendix 7:

Conversion of tin prices from Malaysian ringgits per pikul* to
sterling pounds per metric ton at varying exchange rates

		Exchange rate: Malaysian ringgits/£ sterling			
		3.5	4.0	4.5	5.0
		£ sterling per metric ton			
Malaysian ringgits/pikul	500	2,361	2,066	1,836	1,653
	1,000	4,722	4,132	3,673	3,306
	2,000	9,444	8,264	7,346	6,612
	3,000	14,166	12,396	11,019	9,918

*pikul = 133.33lb

Appendix 8:
Useful addresses

Associations

The Aluminium Federation
Broadway House
Calthorpe Road
Birmingham B15 1TN
United Kingdom
Tel 021 4550311

Bismuth Institute
Rue Brederode 9
1000 Bruxelles
Belgium

The British Non-Ferrous Metals Federation
6 Bathurst Street
London W2 2SD
Tel 01 7237465

Bureau International de la Recuperation (BIR)
Place du Samedi 13- Bte 4
1000 Bruxelles
Belgium
Tel 2 2178251

CIPEC (Intergovernmental Council of Copper
Exporting Countries)
177 Avenue de Roule
92200 Neuilly sur Seine
Paris
France
Tel 1 7581155

Commodities Research Unit
26 Red Lion Square
London WC1 4RL
Tel 01 2427463

Copper Development Association
Orchard House
Mutton Lane
Potters Bar
Herts EN6 3AP
United Kingdom
Tel 01 7750711

General Services Administration
General Services Building
18th and F St NW
Washington DC 20405
USA
Tel 202 6554000

International Lead/Zinc Study Group
Metro House
58 St James's Street
London SW1A 1LD
Tel 01 4999373

International Primary Aluminium Institute
9th Floor
New Zealand House
Haymarket
London SW1
Tel 01 9303051

International Tin Council
1 Oxendon Street
London SW1Y 4EQ
Tel 01 9300321

Minor Metals Traders Association
69 Cannon Street
London EC4N 5AB
Tel 01 2484444

National Association of Recycling Industries
Inc (NARI)
330 Madison Avenue
New York NY 10017
Tel 212 8677336

Roskill Information Services Ltd
2 Clapham Road
London SW9 0JA
Tel 01 5825155

World Bureau of Metal Statistics
41 Doughty Street
London WC1N 2LF
Tel 01 4052771

Zinc Lead and Cadmium Development
Associations
34 Berkeley Square
London W1L 6AJ
Tel 01 4996636

The Minor Metals Traders' Association

Members

ACLI International
Acli Metal & Ore Division
110 Wall Street
New York
NY 10005 USA
Tel 212 9438700 Telex RCA 232261

Ametalco Trading Limited
29 Gresham Street
London EC2V 7DA
Tel 01 6068800 Telex 885541

Ayrton & Partners Ltd
Friendly House
21-24 Chiswell Street
London EC1Y 4SN
Tel 01 6385588 Telex 887648

Basmont Metal Co Ltd
Victoria House
Vernon Place
Southampton Row
London WC1B 4DN
Tel 01 4055065 Telex 27312

Bocmin Metals Ltd
Broadway Chambers
Hammersmith Broadway
London W6
Tel 01 7410661 Telex 934849

Brandeis Goldschmidt & Co Ltd
4 Fore Street
London EC2P 2NU
Tel 01 6385877 Telex 84401

Brookside Metal BV
Vredenburg L24
3511 BB Utrecht
Holland
Tel 30 313851 Telex 40555

Cambridge Metals Limited
7 All Saints Passage
Cambridge CB2 3LS
Tel 0223 312111 Telex 817570

Chloride Metals Ltd
Manor Metal Works
Harrow Manorway
Abbey Wood
London SE2 9RW
Tel 01 3104444 Telex 896948

Cominco (UK) Ltd
50 Finsbury Square
London EC2A 1BD
Tel 01 6384000 Telex 886563

Commodity Analysis Ltd
37-39 St Andrews Hill
London EC4V 5DD
Tel 01 2489571 Telex 883356

Continental Metals Corporation
820 Second Avenue
New York
NY 10011
USA
Tel 212 4219811 Telex 425589

Copalco International Ltd
Suite 354
200 Park Avenue
New York
NY 10017 USA
Tel 212 6977260 Telex 127758

R L Cusick (Metals) Ltd
Cusick House
Church Street
Ware
Herts
Tel 0920 61181 Telex 817395

Entores Ltd
79-83 Chiswell Street
London EC1Y 4TB
Tel 01 6066050 Telex 261932

Erlanger & Co (Commodities) Ltd
Moor House
London Wall
London EC2Y 5ET
Tel 01 6386691 Telex 8813155

Exsud Ltd
237-247 Tottenham Court Road
London W1P 0BU
Tel 01 6314959 Telex 264751

FLT & Metals Ltd
1-5 Long Lane
London EC1A 9HA
Tel 01 6061272 Telex 8811917

Gerald Metals Ltd
Europe House
World Trade Centre
St Katherine-by-the-Tower
London E1 9AA
Tel 01 4810681 Telex 884377

Gill & Duffus Ltd
201 Borough High Street
London SE1 1HW
Tel 01 4077050 Telex 887588

Greendown Trading BV
Bozembocht 23
PO Box 3048
Rotterdam
Holland
Tel 10 13207 Telex 23508

Grondmet
Rochussenstraat 125
Rotterdam
Holland
Tel 10 361933 Telex 21689, 25218

Intsel Ltd
83-87 Gracechurch Street
London EC3V 0AA
Tel 01 6233691 Telex 8811981

AC Israel Woodhouse Co Ltd
21 Mincing Lane
London EC3R 7DN
Tel 01 6233131 Telex 883136, 883139

Lambert Metals Ltd
506-508 Kingsbury Road
London NW9 9HE
Tel 01 2049422 Telex 23844

Leopold Lazarus Ltd
Gotch House
20-34 St Bride Street
London EC4A 4DL
Tel 01 5838060 Telex 265544

Leigh & Sillavan Ltd
Knights Pools
Windmill Street
Macclesfield
Cheshire SK11 7HR
Tel 0625 31331 Telex 668363

Lonconex Ltd
29 Mincing Lane
London EC3R 7EU
Tel 01 6264383 Telex 885016

Maclaine Watson & Co Ltd
2-4 Idol Lane
London EC3R 5DL
Tel 01 2838611 Telex 883854

Arthur Matyas & Co Ltd
Pearl House
746 Finchley Road
London NW11 7TH
Tel 01 4588911 Telex 8812123

Metaleg Metall GmbH
Graf Adolph Strasse 22
4000 Dusseldorf 1
West Germany
Tel 211 631011 Telex 8582610

Metallbodio Ltd
PO Box 296
CH-4010 Basel
Switzerland
Tel 61 238953 Telex 62270

Metramet Ltd
Kingswell 58-62 Heath Street
London NW3 1EN
Tel 01 7941131 Telex 25479

Minor Metals Inc
1 Gulf & Western Plaza
Room 918
New York NY 10023 USA
Tel 212 5418880 Telex 426965

Minwood Metals Ltd
Paterson Road
Finedon Industrial Estate
Wellingborough
Northants
Tel 0933 225766 Telex 311394

Nemco Metal International Ltd
9 Harrowden Road
Brackmills
Northampton NN4 0EB
Tel 0604 66181 Telex 826433

A J Oster Co
50 Sims Avenue
Providence
Rhode Island USA
Tel 401 4213840 Telex WUD 927747

Powell Metals & Chemicals (UK) Inc
62 Hills Road
Cambridge CB2 1LA
Tel 0223 51775 Telex 817669 Powcang

Primetal Italia
20124 Milano
Via Cappellini 16
Italy
Tel 2 667124 Telex 33439

Derek Raphael & Co Ltd
DRC House
2 Cornwall Terrace
Regents Park
London NW1 4QP
Tel 01 4869931 Telex 261916

Redlac Metals Ltd
148 Buckingham Palace Road
London SW1W 9TR
Tel 01 7032276 Telex 888885

Rhonda Metal Co Ltd
Rhonda Works
Perth
Mid-Glamorgan
Wales CF39 9BA
Tel 044 3612881 Telex 49562

Rothmetal Trading Ltd
PO Box 1549
Argus Insurance Building
Wesley Street
Hamilton
Bermuda
Tel 80929 27980 Telex 3368 BA

William Rowland Ltd
Powke Lane
Cradley Heath
Warley
West Midlands B64 5PX
Tel 021 5593031 Telex 331376

Sassoon & Co SA
203 Avenue Louise
PO Box 4
1050 Brussels
Belgium
Tel 2 6406783 Telex 63605

Jack Sharkey & Co Ltd
Middlemore Road
Smethwick
Warley
West Midlands B66 2DP
Tel 021 5587444

Skandinaviska Malm-Och
Metallaktiebolaget
Kungsgatan 6
Box 7547
S-103 93 Stockholm
Sweden
Tel 8 233520 Telex 19552

Sogemet
161 Avenue Charles de Gaulle
92202 Neuilly sur Seine
France
Tel 1 6375760 Telex 820242

Spencer Metals & Minerals Ltd
25 London Road
Newbury
Berks, United Kingdom

Steetley Chemicals Ltd
Berk House
PO Box 56
Basing View
Basingstoke
Hants RG21 2EG
Tel 0256 29292 Telex 858371

Sterling Enterprises Metals Ltd
Sterling House
328 Holloway Road
London N7 7HJ
Tel 01 6077381 Telex 27325

Tennant Trading Ltd
9 Harp Lane
Lower Thames Street
London EC3R 6DR
Tel 01 6264533 Telex 884724

Trans-World Metals Ltd
Walsingham House
35 Seething Lane
London EC3N 4EL
Tel 01 4805701 Telex 8951322

Unimet GmbH
Stahl, Rohre und Metalle
Cecilienallee 21
4000 Dusseldorf 30
West Germany
Tel 211 450914 Telex 08582622

H A Watson & Co Ltd
119-120 High Street
Stourbridge
West Midlands DY 8 1DT
Tel 03843 77801 Telex 337034

Rene Weil SA
77 Rue de Monceau
75008 Paris
France
Tel 1 5630488 Telex 280445

Wheatstock Ltd
4 Fore Street
London EC2Y 5EH
Tel 01 5887081 Telex 8814900

Wogen Resources Ltd
17 Devonshire Street
London W1
Tel 01 5805762 Telex 28820

Journals

American Metal Market
7 East 12th Street
New York NY 10003
Tel 212 7414000

Metal Bulletin Ltd
45-46 Lower Marsh
London SE1 7RG
Tel 01 6330525

Metals Week
McGraw-Hill Inc
1221 Avenue of the Americas
New York NY 10020
Tel 212 9971221

Tin International
Tin Publications Ltd
7 High Road
London W4 2NE
Tel 01 9959277

London Metal Exchange

The following are member companies of the
London Metal Exchange. *These are ring
dealing members.

Amalgamated Metal Corp Ltd
Adelaide House
London Bridge
London EC4R 9DT
Tel 01 6264521 Telex 888701
Cable Amalgameco London

Amalgamated Metal Trading Ltd*
2 Metal Exchange Buildings
Leadenhall Avenue
London EC3V 1LD
Tel 01 6264521 Telex 888704

Ambores Ltd
27 Marylebone Road
London NW1 5JS
Tel 01 4864642

Ametalco Ltd
29 Gresham Street
London EC2V 7DA
Tel 01 6068800 Telex 885541
Cable Nucliform London EC2

Ametalco Merchanting Ltd
1 Noble Street
London EC2V 7DA
Tel 01 6068800 Telex 885541

Ametalco Trading Ltd*
29 Gresham Street
London EC2V 7DA
Tel 01 6068800 Telex 885541
Cable Nucliform London EC2

AM & S Europe Ltd
PO Box 237
1 Redcliff Street
Bristol BS99 7EA
Tel 0272 290421 Telex 449502

Anglo Chemical Metals Ltd*
Gillett House
55 Basinghall Street
London EC2V 5HN
Tel 01 6060811 Telex 886767

Anglo Chemical & Ore Co Ltd
Gillett House
55 Basinghall Street
London EC2V 5HN
Tel 01 6060811 Telex 885168

Anmercosa Sales Ltd
40 Holborn Viaduct
London EC1P 1AJ
Tel 01 3531545 Telex 264791

Morris Ashby Ltd
10 Philpot Lane
London EC3M 8AA
Tel 01 6268071 Telex 886170

Associated Lead Manufacturers Ltd*
Clements House
14-18 Gresham Street
London EC2V 7AT
Tel 01 6064400 Telex 884141
Cable Associlead London

Astra Metals Ltd
Northway House
High Road
Whetstone
London N20 9LP
Tel 01 4464381 Telex 267401

Austral Metals Ltd
9 Park Place
St James's
London SW1A 1LX
Tel 01 4938474 Telex 23672

Ayrton & Partners Ltd
Friendly House
21-24 Chiswell Street
London EC1Y 4SN
Tel 01 6385588 Telex 887648

Bache Halsey Stuart (London) Ltd
Plantation House
Fenchurch Street
London EC3M 3EP
Tel 01 6234646 Telex 883251

Bassett Smith & Co Ltd
9 Harp Lane
Lower Thames Street
London EC3R 6DR
Tel 01 6264533 Telex 884754

Henry Bath & Son Ltd*
Market Buildings
Mincing Lane
London EC3R 7DA
Tel 01 6261981 Telex 887700
Cable Bathota

BICC Ltd
PO Box 1
Prescot
Merseyside L34 5SZ
Tel 051 4266571 Telex 627364

BICC Metals Ltd
PO Box 1
Prescot
Merseyside L34 5SZ
Tel 051 4266571 Telex 627364

Billiton-Enthoven Metals Ltd*
Colonial House
Mincing Lane
London EC3R 7DP
Tel 01 6232080 Telex 887939

Billiton Metal & Ores (UK) Ltd
3-4 Lincolns Inn Fields
London WC2A 3AA
Tel 01 8317252 Telex 885737

Boustead Davis (Metal Brokers) Ltd
5 Whittington Avenue
London EC3V 1LE
Tel 01 6263538 Telex 883928

M C Brackenbury & Co
19 St Mary-at-Hill
London EC3R 8EE
Tel 01 6235701/5707 Telex 883304

Brandeis Goldschmidt & Co Ltd*
4 Fore Street
London EC2P 2NU
Tel 01 6385877 Telex 884401

Britannia Lead Co Ltd
Adelaide House
King William Street
London EC4R 9DX
Tel 01 6267446 Telex 884210

British American Metals Co Ltd
French Railways House
178-179 Piccadilly
London W1V 0QH
Tel 01 4937835 Telex 27380

Cerro Metals (UK) Ltd*
Devonshire House
Devonshire Row
London EC2M 4JX
Tel 01 3778050 Telex 887276
Cable Cerro UK

Chloride Metals Ltd
Felixstowe Road
Abbey Wood
London SE2 9RW
Tel 01 3104444 Telex 896948

Cominco (UK) Ltd*
50 Finsbury Square
London EC2A 1DD
Tel 01 6384000 Telex 886563
Cable Tadanac London

The Commercial Metal Co Ltd*
Park House
16 Finsbury Circus
London EC2M 7DJ
Tel 01 6385789 Telex 887410, 887419
Cable Cometalco

Commodity Analysis Ltd
37-39 St Andrews Hill
London EC4V 5DD
Tel 01 2489571 Telex 883356

Conti Commodity Services Ltd
Europe House
World Trade Centre
London E1 9AA
Tel 01 4883232 Telex 887438
Cable TGR/CCSG

Continental Ore Europe Ltd*
18 Rood Lane
London EC3M 8BS
Tel 01 6233621 Telex 886269

C Czarnikow Ltd
PO Box 602
66 Mark Lane
London EC3P 3EA
Tel 01 4806677 Telex 885011

Delta Metal Co Ltd
1 Kingsway
London WC2B 6XF
Tel 01 8363535 Telex 27762
Cable Delta Kings Ldn

Delta Rod Holdings Ltd
Greets Green Road
West Bromwich
West Midlands B70 9ER
Tel 021 5536188 Telex 336661
Cable Extrusion West Bromwich

Derby & Co Ltd
Moor House
London Wall
London EC2Y 5JE
Tel 01 6382876 Telex 883801
Cable Plativet London EC2

Dietiker Metals (UK) Ltd
48 Mount Street
London W1
Tel 01 3532151 Telex 887734/35
Cable Dmet UK

Drexel Burnham Lambert Ltd
Winchester House
77 London Wall
London EC2N 1BE
Tel 01 6283200 Telex 884995, 884845
Cable Coburnham London EC2

Enfield Rolling Mills Ltd
Millmarsh Lane
Brimsdown
Enfield
Middlesex
Tel 01 8041255 Telex 22869
Cable Rolenmil

Engelhard Sales Ltd
St Nicholas House
St Nicholas Road
Sutton
Surrey
Tel 01 6438080 Telex 22317
Cable Platmetals Sutton Surrey

H J Enthoven & Sons Ltd
Darley Dale Smelter
South Darley
nr Matlock
Derbyshire DE4 2LP
Tel 062 9833291 Telex 377757

Entores (Metal Brokers) Ltd*
City Wall House
79-83 Chiswell Street
London EC1Y 4TB
Tel 01 6066050 Telex 887621

Exsud Ltd
237-247 Tottenham Court Road
London W1P 0BU
Tel 01 6314959 Telex 2645751
Cable Exsud London

Frank Fehr & Co Ltd
Prince Rupert House
64 Queen Street
London EC4R 1ER
Tel 01 2485066 Telex 888960
Cable Fairfrall London

Fergusson Wild & Co Ltd
3 St Helen's Place
London EC3A 6DB
Tel 01 5887022 Telex 883503

Gardner Lohmann Ltd
6 Laurence Pountney Hill
London EC4R 0BL
Tel 01 6268086 Telex 884458, 886388

Gerald Metals Ltd*
Europe House
World Trade Centre
St Katherine-by-the-Tower
London E1 9AA
Tel 01 4810681 Telex 883869
Cable GMET London

Gill & Duffus Ltd*
St Dunstan's House
201 Borough High Street
London SE1 1HW
Tel 01 4077050 Telex 887588

Gill & Duffus (Metals) Ltd
St Dunstan's House
201 Borough High Street
London SE1 1HW
Tel 01 4077050 Telex 887588

M Golodetz Ltd
29 Mincing Lane
London EC3R 7EE
Tel 01 6264383 Telex 855016

M Golodetz (Overseas) Ltd
Aldwych House
71-91 Aldwych
London WC2B 4HN
Tel 01 2428888 Telex 23567
Cable Goloseas London WC2

Harlow & Jones Ltd
St Albans House
59 Haymarket
London SW1
Tel 01 8398030 Telex 917691
Cable Harjones

Heathfield Proprietary Ltd
9 Park Place, St James's
London SW1
Tel 01 4938474 Telex 23672

IMI Ltd
PO Box 216
Kynoch Works, Witton
Birmingham B6 7BA
United Kingdom
Tel 021 3564848 Telex 366771
Cable Kynoch Birmingham

Imperial Chemical Industries Ltd
Imperial Chemical House
Millbank
London SW1P 3JF
Tel 01 8344444 Telex 21324
Cable Impkemix

Inter Commodities Ltd
5 Lloyds Avenue
London EC3N 3DS
Tel 01 4819827 Telex 884962

International Metals Ltd
56 Artillery Lane
London E1 7LS
Tel 01 3770660 Telex 8954191

Intsel Ltd*
4th Floor
85 Gracechurch Street
London EC3V 0AA
Tel 01 6233691 Telex 8811981
Cable Intsel London EC3

A C Israel Woodhouse Co Ltd
21 Mincing Lane
London EC3P 7DN
Tel 01 6233131 Telex 88742
Cable Acicowood Ldn

Jacob Metals Ltd
8 Waterloo Place
St James's
London SW1Y 4AH
Tel 01 9306953 Telex 918034
Cable Metaljacob

Johnson Matthey Commodities Ltd
5 Lloyds Avenue
London EC3N 3DB
Tel 01 4813181 Telex 884312

Johnson & Nephew (Non-Ferrous) Ltd
Denby Dale Road
Wakefield, Yorks
United Kingdom
Tel 0924 75172 Telex 557274

G W Joynson & Co Ltd
14 Trinity Square
London EC3N 4ES
Tel 01 4806921 Telex 885346
Cable Warrior

Leopold Lazarus Ltd*
Gotch House
20-34 St Bride Street
London EC4A 4DL
Tel 01 5838060 Telex 24801
Cable Orminaz

Leigh & Sillivan Group Ltd
Knights Pool,Windmill Street
Macclesfield
Cheshire SK11 7HR
United Kingdom
Tel 0625 31331 Telex 688363
Cable Sillivan Macclesfield

Lewis & Peat (Metals) Ltd
32 St Mary-at-Hill
London EC3R 8DH
Tel 01 6233111 Telex 883983

Lonconex Ltd*
29 Mincing Lane
London EC3R 7EU
Tel 01 6264383 Telex 885016
Cable Lonconex London EC3

J Lowenstein & Co Ltd
Lometa House,12-14 River Road
Barking
Essex IG11 0DG
United Kingdom
Tel 01 5911114 Telex 897224
Cable Lometa

D B Mack Ltd
Plantation House
Mincing Lane
London EC3M 3PH
Tel 01 6260101 Telex 885977

Maclaine Watson & Co Ltd*
2-4 Idol Lane
London EC3R 5DL
Tel 01 2838611 Telex 884328
Cable Macwat London EC3

Metallgesellschaft Ltd*
19-21 Gt Tower Street
London EC3R 5AQ
Tel 01 6264221 Telex 888971
Cable Metallbank London

Metdist Ltd*
Barrington House
59-67 Gresham Street
London EC2V 7EY
Tel 01 6060463 Telex 888248

Metro Metal Traders Ltd
Station House
Harrow Road
Wembley HA9 6DE
Tel 01 9034971 Telex 923548
Cable Metromet Ldn

Moutafian Commodities Ltd
2-4 Eastcheap
London EC3M 1AL
Tel 01 6233311 Telex 884412
Cable Moutafian London

Noranda Sales Corp of Canada Ltd
New Zealand House
Haymarket
London SW1Y 4TH
Tel 01 8397601 Telex 24666
Cable Noranda London

Jeremy Oates Ltd
16 Monument Street
London EC3R 8AJ
Tel 01 6237301 Telex 888264

Pacol Ltd
47 Mark Lane
London EC3R 7QX
Tel 01 6231000 Telex 888712
Cable Pacolanter

Philipp & Lion*
Moor House
London Wall
London EC2Y 5AR
Tel 01 6783060 Telex 888555

Pirelli General Cable Works Ltd
PO Box 4
Western Esplanade
Southampton SO9 7AE
Tel 0703 20384 Telex 47522

J H Rayner (Mincing Lane) Ltd*
50 Mark Lane
London EC3R 7QJ
Tel 01 4810144 Telex 888161

Marc Rich & Co Ltd
49 Wigmore Street
London W1H 9LE
Tel 01 9354455 Telex 21223/4

Richmond Metal Co Ltd
Delbow Road
North Feltham Trading Estate
Faggs Road
Feltham, Middlesex
United Kingdom
Tel 01 8900981 Telex 934857

Henry Rogers (London) Ltd
9 Harp Lane
Great Tower Street
London EC3R 6DR
Tel 01 6264533 Telex 884724

Sharps, Pixley Ltd*
10 Rood Lane
London EC3M 8BB
Tel 01 6238000 Telex 883319

Shearson Hayden Stone Ltd
St Alphage House
2 Fore Street
London EC2Y 5DA
Tel 01 5887505 Telex 888881

Sogemin (Metals) Ltd*
10th Floor
Stock Exchange Building
Throgmorton Street
London EC2N 1EL
Tel 01 6286421 Telex 885244

Tennant Trading (Metals) Ltd*
9 Harp Lane
Lower Thames Street
London EC3R 6DR
Tel 01 6264533 Telex 887604

H P Thompson & Sons Ltd*
8 Lloyds Avenue
London EC3N 3AB
Tel 01 4807951 Telex 8951635
Cable Knilomet London EC3

Triland Metals Ltd*
Bow Bells House
Broad Street
London EC4M 9BQ
Tel 01 2365551 Telex 888677
Cable Trimet London EC4

Wallace Brothers Commodities Ltd
108 Fenchurch Street
London EC3M 5HP
Tel 01 4818671 Telex 887442

H A Watson & Co Ltd
11 Mansfield Road, Rotherham
South Yorkshire S20 2DR
United Kingdom
Tel 0709 74293 Telex 547393

Wilson Smithett and Cope*
32 St Mary-at-Hill
London EC3R 8DH
Tel 01 6239333 Telex 886818
Cable Infados

Wogen Resources Ltd
17 Devonshire Street
London W1N 1FS
Tel 01 5805762 Telex 28820

Woodhouse Drake and Carey Ltd
Three Quays, Tower Hill
London EC3R 6EP
Tel 01 6237575 Telex 886271
Cable Progne

Rudolf Wolff and Co Ltd*
Knollys House, 11 Byward Street
London EC3R 5ED
Tel 01 6268765 Telex 885034
Cable Occasion London

Commodity Exchange Inc (COMEX), New York, NY 10048

The following are member firms as of February 1980. *These are Members, COMEX Clearing Association, Inc.

Acli International Commodity Services Inc*
110 Wall Street
New York
New York 10005

Acli International Inc*
717 Westchester Avenue
White Plains
New York 10604

Adachi Gold Co Ltd
c/o Gusrae, Green & Kaplan
67 Wall Street
New York
New York 10005

Amax Copper Inc*
200 Park Avenue
New York
New York 10017

Amax Inc*
Two Greenwich Plaza
Greenwich
Connecticut 06830, USA

Ametalco Inc*
200 Park Avenue
New York
New York 10017

Ansor Corporation
1351 Washington Boulevard
Stamford
Connecticut 06902, USA

J Aron & Company Inc*
160 Water Street
New York
New York 10038

J Aron Commodities Corporation*
160 Water Street
New York
New York 10038

Asarco Incorporated
120 Broadway
New York
New York 10005

Associated Metals & Minerals Corporation
30 Rockefeller Plaza
New York
New York 10020

Bache Halsey Stuart Shields Inc*
100 Gold Street
New York
New York 10038

Balfour, Maclaine Inc*
88 Pine Street
Wall Street Plaza
New York
New York 10005

Banco Nacional de Mexico SA
Isabel La Catolica No 44
Mexico 1, DF

Bear, Stearns & Co*
55 Water Street
New York
New York 10041

A G Becker-Kipnis & Co*
209 South LaSalle Street
Chicago
Illinois 60604, USA

Bell & Company, Stanley B
Four World Trade Center
New York
New York 10048

Michael Belmont & Co
Four World Trade Center
New York
New York 10048

Billiton-Enthoven Metals Ltd
Colonial House
Mincing Lane
London EC3R 7DR
England

Billiton Metals & Ores USA Inc
600 Fifth Avenue
New York
New York 10020

Blyth Eastman Dillon & Co Inc*
1221 Avenue of the Americas
New York
New York 10020

Boys, Investment & Trade Ltd
PO Box 3125 Ch-1951
Sion
Switzerland

Brandeis, Goldschmidt & Co (Commodities)
Inc*
919 Third Avenue
New York
New York 10022

Brandeis, Goldschmidt & Co Inc*
919 Third Avenue
New York
New York 10022

Alvin Brodsky & Co
Four World Trade Center
New York
New York 10048

Brody, White & Co Inc*
Four World Trade Center
Suite 5200
New York
New York 10048

Bullion Exchange & Trading Co Ltd
PO Box 2353
CH 1002 Lausanne
4 Avenue De La Gare
CH 1003 Lausanne
Switzerland

Cargill Investor Services Inc*
141 West Jackson Boulevard
Chicago
Illinois 60604

Cerro Sales Corporation*
250 Park Avenue
New York
New York 10017

Clayton Brokerage Co of St Louis Inc*
7701 Forsyth Boulevard
Suite 300
St Louis
Missouri 63105, USA

Commodities Corporation Inc
Mount Lucus Road
Princeton
New Jersey 08540, USA

Commodity International Co*
84 William Street
New York
New York 10038

Conti Commodity Services Inc*
Four World Trade Center
Suite 774, SE Plaza Building
New York
New York 10048

Continental Grain Co*
277 Park Avenue
New York
New York 10017

Cowen & Co
One Battery Park Plaza
New York
New York 10004

Dean Witter Reynolds Inc*
45 Montgomery Street
San Francisco
California 94106, USA

Drexel, Burnham Lambert Inc*
60 Broad Street
New York
New York 10004

Easton & Company *
One State Street Plaza
New York
New York 10005

A G Edwards & Sons Inc *
One North Jefferson
St Louis
Missouri 63103

Eisen & Blum Inc *
141 West Jackson Boulevard
Chicago
Illinois 60604, USA

Engelhard Minerals & Chemical Corporation *
1221 Avenue of the Americas
New York
New York 10020

Fahnestock & Company *
110 Wall Street
New York
New York 10005

Federbush & Co
Four World Trade Center
New York
New York 10048

Floor Broker Associates
Four World Trade Center
New York
New York 10048

Felix J Forlenza & Co
Four World Trade Center
New York
New York 10048

Walter N Frank & Co
14 Wall Street
New York
New York 10005

Ray E Friedman & Company *
222 South Riverside Plaza
Chicago
Illinois 60606, USA

Gerald Commodity Services Inc *
High Ridge Park
PO Box 10134
Stamford
Connecticut 06904, USA

Gerald Metals Inc *
High Ridge Park
PO Box 10134
Stamford
Connecticut 06904, USA

GK Technologies Inc
500 W Putnam Avenue
Greenwich
Connecticut 06830, USA

Goldman, Sachs & Co *
55 Broad Street
New York
New York 10004

Granger & Company
111 Broadway
New York
New York 10006

Willhelm Grillo Handelsgesellschaft
Am Grillo Park 5
Duisburg-Hamborn
West Germany

Handy & Harman
850 Third Avenue
New York
New York 10022

Harmon, Lichtenstein & Co
Four World Trade Center, Room 7170
New York
New York 10048

Heinold Commodities Inc *
222 South Riverside Plaza
Chicago
Illinois 60606, USA

Herzfeld & Stern
30 Broad Street
New York
New York 10004

E F Hutton & Co Inc *
One Battery Park Plaza
New York
New York 10004

Insilco Corporation
1000 Research Parkway
Meriden
Connecticut 06450, USA

Intramet Corporation
437 Madison Avenue
New York
New York 10022

Intsel Corporation *
825 Third Avenue
New York
New York 10022

Johnson Matthey Bankers Ltd
5 Lloyds Avenue
London EC3N 3DB
England

Jones Commodities, D E
Four World Trade Center
New York
New York 10048

Klein & Co*
170 Broadway, Room 806
New York
New York 10006

Lehman Brothers Kuhn Loeb Inc
56 Water Street
New York
New York 10041

Levy Commodities*
222 South Riverside Plaza
Chicago
Illinois 60606, USA

Lewis & Peat Trading Inc
Wall Street Plaza
New York
New York 10005

Leytess Metal & Chemical Corporation
500 Fifth Avenue
New York
New York 10036

Lincolnwood Inc*
141 West Jackson Boulevard
Chicago
Illinois 60604, USA

Lonconex Ltd
29 Mincing Lane
London EC3
England

Lonray (Sugar) Inc*
77 Water Street
New York
New York 10005

Macro International Group Inc*
115 Broadway, Suite 1615
New York
New York 10006

Maduff & Sons Inc*
175 West Jackson Boulevard
Chicago
Illinois 60604, USA

McCormick Commodities Inc
141 West Jackson Boulevard
Chicago
Illinois 60604, USA

Merrill Lynch, Pierce, Fenner & Smith Inc*
One Liberty Plaza
165 Broadway
New York
New York 10006

Metal Traders Inc*
666 Fifth Avenue
New York
New York 10019

Minemet Clearing Inc*
450 Park Avenue
New York
New York 10022

Mintz-Marcus & Co
Four World Trade Center
New York
New York 10048

Mocatta Metals Corporation*
Four World Trade Center, Suite 5200
New York
New York 10048

Samuel Montagu & Co Ltd
114 Old Broad Street
London EC2P 2HY
England

NCZ Commodities Inc
505 Park Avenue
New York
New York 10022

NMR Metals Inc
45 Rockefeller Plaza, Suite 3225
New York
New York 10020

NRT Metals Inc
576 Fifth Avenue
New York
New York 10036

OCC Commodity Inc*
605 Third Avenue
New York
New York 10016

Oppenheimer & Co Inc
One New York Plaza
New York
New York 10004

Ore & Chemical Corporation, The*
605 Third Avenue
New York
New York 10016

Paine, Webber, Jackson & Curtis Inc*
25 Broad Street, 19th Floor
New York
New York 10004

Peters & Co*
141 West Jackson Boulevard
Chicago
Illinois 60604, USA

Philipp & Lion
Moor House
London Wall
London EC2Y 5AR
England

Precious Metals Corporation of America*
Four World Trade Center, Suite 9468
New York
New York 10048

Primary Industries Corporation*
666 Fifth Avenue
New York
New York 10019

Primary Metal & Mineral Corporation*
666 Fifth Avenue
New York
New York 10019

Pro-Met Trading Co
30 East 65th Street
New York
New York 10021

Redel Trading Co Inc*
140 Cedar Street
New York
New York 10006

Refinemet International Co
One Main Street
Mapleville
Rhode Island 02839, USA

Republic Clearing Corporation*
450 Fifth Avenue
New York
New York 10018

Marc Rich & Co Inc
280 Park Avenue
New York
New York 10017

Richardson Securities Inc*
40 Wall Street
New York
New York 10005

Rosenthal & Company*
141 West Jackson Boulevard
Chicago
Illinois 60604, USA

L F Rothschild, Unterberg, Towbin
55 Water Street
New York
New York 10041

R J Rouse & Co Ltd
Dunster House, Mincing Lane
London EC3R 7TH
England

RTB Incorporated*
PO Box 4086
Greenwich
Connecticut 06830, USA

Sabin Commodities
140 Cedar Street
New York
New York 10006

Mel Schnell & Co
Four World Trade Center
New York
New York 10048

Howard Schwartz & Co
Four World Trade Center, 8th Floor
New York
New York 10048

Servonet Corporation
540 Madison Avenue, 30th Floor
New York
New York 10022

Sharps, Pixley Inc*
100 Wall Street
New York
New York 10005

Shearson-Loeb Rhoades Inc
One Western Union, International Plaza
New York
New York 10004

Silgo Corporation
160 Broadway, Room 903
New York
New York 10038

James Sinclair Commodities
90 Broad Street
New York
New York 10004

Smith Barney, Harris Upham & Co Inc*
1345 Avenue of the Americas
New York
New York 10019

Spiral Metal Co Inc
515 Madison Avenue
New York
New York 10022

Lee B Stern & Co Ltd
141 West Jackson Boulevard
Chicago
Illinois 60604, USA

Stern & Stern Securities Inc
110 Wall Street
New York
New York 10005

T & S Commodities*
Four World Trade Center
New York
New York 10048

Telic Trading Corporation
Four World Trade Center
New York
New York 10048

C Tennant Sons & Co of New York*
PO Box 9300, Section 40
Minneapolis
Minnesota 55440, USA

Thomson, McKinnon Securities Inc*
One New York Plaza
New York
New York 10004

Toyamamerica Bussan Inc
Four World Trade Center, Suite 9222
New York
New York 10048

Trans World Metals Inc*
770 Lexington Avenue
New York
New York 10021

Albert Trostel & Sons Company
800 North Marshall Street
Milwaukee
Wisconsin 53202, USA

Truebner & Co Inc*
130 John Street
New York
New York 10038

United Equities Commodities Company*
160 Broadway
New York
New York 10038

UV Industries Inc
437 Madison Avenue
New York
New York 10022

Volkart Brokerage Inc*
120 Wall Street
New York
New York 10005

Wark Trading Company
Four World Trade Center
New York
New York 10048

Rudolf Wolff Commodity Brokers Inc*
295 Madison Avenue
New York
New York 10017

Woodhouse Drake & Carey Inc
120 John Street
New York
New York 10038